Reducing error and influencing behaviour

HSE BOOKS

HSG48

Contents

Introduction

This guidance is aimed at managers with health and safety responsibilities, health and safety professionals and employee safety representatives.

The message is that proper consideration of 'human factors' is a key ingredient of effective health and safety management. Human factors is a broad field and organisations may have viewed it in the past as being too complex or difficult to do anything about. This guidance aims to overcome such fears by providing practical help on how to tackle some of the important issues.

The guidance:

■ explains how human error and behaviour can impact on health and safety;
■ shows how human behaviour and other factors in the workplace can affect the physical and mental health of workers;
■ provides practical ideas on what you can do to identify, assess and control risks arising from the human factor; and
■ includes illustrative case studies to show how other organisations have tackled different human problems at work.

The format of the publication is as follows:

Chapter 1 provides an introduction to human factors. **Chapter 2** looks at types of human failures, their causes and ways of reducing them. **Chapter 3** considers how to improve health and safety at work through better design of tasks, equipment, procedures and warnings. **Chapter 4** looks at some key operational issues: shiftwork and fatigue, shift communication, risk perception and behaviour, and health and safety culture. **Chapter 5** provides some hints on how to get started. **Chapter 6** presents a series of case studies which illustrate practical cost-effective solutions to real human factors problems. Tables enable you to read only those cases which are most relevant to your organisation and problem area. Some of the approaches shown in this guidance represent 'good practice' rather than what is strictly required by legislation.

The guidance cannot cover every aspect of human factors. It introduces some key influences on peoples' behaviour and work performance which need to be included in a health and safety management system. References are given including references to general books on human factors. A list of relevant professional societies and a glossary of terms is also provided.

This publication is a revision of guidance originally published in 1989 *Human factors in industrial safety*. This major revision reflects improvements in our understanding of human error and human behaviour at work and the need to carry out risk assessments which take account of these issues.

CHAPTER ONE

What are 'human factors'?

The HSE definition is: 'Human factors refer to environmental, organisational and job factors, and human and individual characteristics which influence behaviour at work in a way which can affect health and safety'. A simple way to view human factors is to think about three aspects: the job, the individual and the organisation and how they impact on people's health and safety-related behaviour.

The job - Tasks should be designed in accordance with ergonomic principles to take into account limitations and strengths in human performance. Matching the job to the person will ensure that they are not overloaded and that the most effective contribution to the business results. *Physical match* includes the design of the whole workplace and working environment. *Mental match* involves the individual's information and decision-making requirements, as well as their perception of the tasks and risks. Mismatches between job requirements and people's capabilities provide the potential for human error.

The individual - People bring to their job personal attitudes, skills, habits and personalities which can be strengths or weaknesses depending on the task demands. Individual characteristics influence behaviour in complex and significant ways. Their effects on task performance may be negative and may not always be mitigated by job design. Some characteristics such as personality are fixed and cannot be changed. Others, such as skills and attitudes, may be changed or enhanced.

The organisation - Organisational factors have the greatest influence on individual and group behaviour, yet they are often overlooked during the design of work and during investigation of accidents and incidents. Organisations need to establish their own positive health and safety culture. The culture needs to promote employee involvement and commitment at all levels, emphasising that deviation from established health and safety standards is not acceptable.

Figure 1 lists some of the key issues for each area. By thinking about these aspects you are asking questions about:

- What are people being asked to do and where (the task and its characteristics)?
- Who is doing it (the individual and their competence)?
- Where are they working (the organisation and its attributes)?

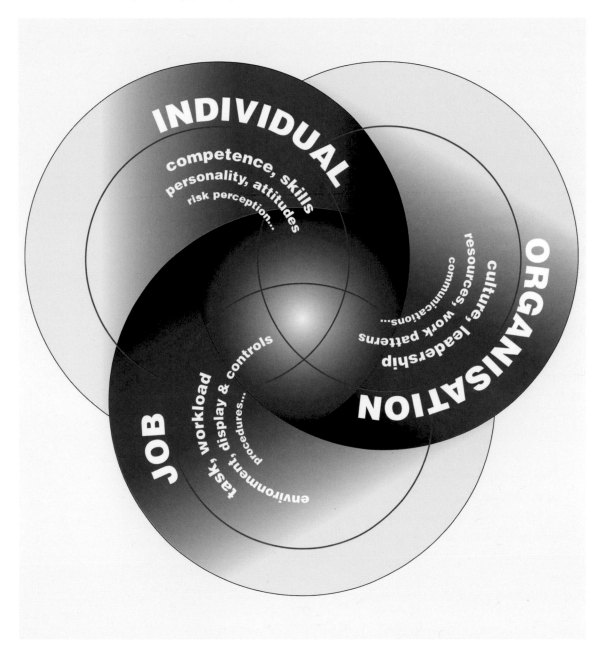

Figure 1 *Human factors in occupational health and safety*

Why should I be interested in human factors issues at work?

Careful consideration of human factors at work can reduce the number of accidents and cases of occupational ill-health. It can also pay dividends in terms of a more efficient and effective workforce.

Accidents can occur through people's involvement with their work. As technical systems have become more reliable, the focus has turned to human causes of accidents. It is estimated that up to 80% of accidents may be attributed, at least in part, to the actions or omissions of people. This is not surprising since people are involved throughout the life cycle of an organisation, from design through to operation, maintenance, management and demolition. Many accidents are blamed on the actions or omissions of an individual who was directly involved in operational or maintenance work. This typical but short-sighted response ignores the fundamental failures which led to the accident. These are usually rooted deeper in the organisation's design, management and decision-making functions.

Work has an impact on people's health as well as on their safety. A positive work experience leads to job satisfaction and contributes to physical and mental well-being. Well-designed tasks and working environments that suit people's individual skills and capabilities can help here. Physical health problems can result from lost-time injuries such as slips and falls, and from manual handling problems. Mental well-being can be affected if someone witnesses a traumatic event, suffers bullying or violence at work, or experiences stress at work.

How do I know if these problems exist in my organisation?

You will know you need to think about human factors issues at work by looking out for some relevant indicators like those given in Box A.

> Accidents involving staff, contractors or visitors where 'human error' is given as a cause
> Occupational health reports of mental or physical ill-health
> High absenteeism or sickness rates
> High staff turnover levels
> Low level of, or changes in, compliance with health and safety rules
> Behaviour or performance issues identified in risk assessments
> Complaints from staff about working conditions or job design

Box A *Some indicators of human factors problems*

Isn't it just about people 'taking more care'?

No. It is quite wrong to believe that telling people to take more care is the answer to these problems. While it is reasonable to expect people to pay attention and take care at work, relying on this is not enough to control risks. Box B shows what can happen if complacency about risks is combined with a belief that 'taking care' is a suitable control measure.

A farm worker was crushed under the wheel of a manure spreader which was being reversed between a building and a retaining wall for a distance of about ten metres.

The driver was asked by the farm worker to move the tractor and spreader to allow access for cattle into a yard. He agreed to move it and intended to reverse it into another yard. When he got into the tractor, the farm worker was standing by the nearside of the tractor. He started the engine and looked over his right shoulder and reversed. After four or five metres he heard a scream and found the worker lying under the nearside of the spreader in front of the wheel. A witness had apparently seen the farm worker fall under the wheel.

The ground was very muddy and the soles of the farm worker's boots had become smooth. The tractor was large and not fitted with rear view mirrors as it was not used on the highway.

Everyone (farm managers and employees) were complacent about the risks in reversing equipment and believed that if everyone 'took care' no accidents would happen. In this case there were a number of steps which could have been taken to reduce the risks, such as the provision of mirrors on the tractor, and checking and replacing of boots. However, these steps would not be implemented unless farm managers and employees took a more positive attitude to risk reduction.

Box B *Employee crushed by reversing manure spreader*

This seems a very broad topic area, where should I start?

Don't be discouraged by the breadth of issues that are covered by human factors. This guidance will provide you with practical information to help you start to manage human factors in your organisation. In particular it should help you to make progress in addressing human factors in four main areas:

- during risk assessments;
- when analysing incidents, accidents and near misses;
- in design and procurement; and
- in certain aspects of day-to-day health and safety management.

It is a continual challenge to manage the risks to and from people at work so that they remain safe and healthy. Improving health and safety cannot rely just on improvements in technical and system factors. You need to tackle some of the important 'people' issues too.

Isn't this going to be costly?

Many improvements will be at minimal cost and the ideas may already exist in your organisation. The set of case studies in Chapter 6 show you how straightforward many human factors changes can be. Even relatively small changes to tasks and the working environment can improve health and safety as well as productivity and quality.

Should I seek the views of the workforce and their representatives?

Yes, this is vital. Both safety representatives and other staff know about their job and working conditions. They will have insights into how this impacts on their health and safety. They will be able to help you to identify key issues and may already have suggestions for improvements. You will need to prioritise these issues and allocate appropriate resources to carry through the actions. Proper planning before implementing changes includes consulting the workforce and their representatives. This will usually lead to any changes being introduced more easily and accepted more readily. Afterwards you will also need to check and review that the changes have been effective.

What kind of control measures are possible?

A range of control measures are available including: workplace precautions, risk control systems, and management arrangements.

Adequate workplace precautions have to be provided and maintained to prevent harm to the people at risk. These precautions include: procedures and warnings, safe systems of work, controls on equipment, alarms, safety instructions, communications arrangements, and machine guards. All of these need to be designed with the human in mind to make sure that they are used correctly and reliably. Ergonomic changes to the task and the working environment also help to reduce risks and can improve the physical and mental well-being of the workforce.

Risk control systems are the basis for ensuring that adequate workplace precautions are provided and maintained. Most of the activities where risk control systems are needed will involve people, eg maintenance, routine and non-routine operations, recruitment and selection, demolition, dealing with emergencies. Looking at ways of improving the human factors aspects of these activities, eg through training, selection, and job design, will enhance risk control.

A set of management processes is necessary to organise, plan, control and monitor the design and implementation of the risk control systems. HSE's publication *Successful health and safety management*[1] provides advice in this area.

KEY MESSAGES

Consideration of 'human factors' is a key ingredient of effective health and safety management. It involves:

- thinking about relevant job, individual and organisational aspects;

- addressing human factors in risk assessment, during accident investigation, in design and procurement and in day-to-day operations;

- involving the workforce and their representatives; and

- selecting from a range of effective control measures.

CHAPTER TWO

Understanding human failure

Human failure and accidents

Over the last 20 years we have learnt much more about the origins of human failure. We can now challenge the commonly held belief that incidents and accidents are the result of a 'human error' by a worker in the 'front line'. Attributing incidents to 'human error' has often been seen as a sufficient explanation in itself and something which is beyond the control of managers. This view is no longer acceptable to society as a whole. Organisations must recognise that they need to consider human factors as a distinct element which must be recognised, assessed and managed effectively in order to control risks.

Table 1 *Some illustrative major accidents*

Accident, industry and date	Consequences	Human contribution and other causes
Three Mile Island *Nuclear industry* 1979	Serious damage to core of nuclear reactor.	Operators failed to diagnose a stuck open valve due to poor design of control panel, distraction of 100 alarms activating, inadequate operator training. Maintenance failures had occurred before but no steps had been taken to prevent them recurring.
King's Cross Fire *Transport sector* 1987	A fire at this underground station in London killed 31 people.	A discarded cigarette probably set fire to grease and rubbish underneath one of the escalators. Organisational changes had resulted in poor escalator cleaning. The fire took hold because of the wooden escalator, the failure of water fog equipment and inadequate fire and emergency training of staff. There was a culture which viewed fires as inevitable.

Table 1 *Some illustrative major accidents (continued)*

Accident, industry and date	Consequences	Human contribution and other causes
Clapham Junction *Transport sector* 1988	35 people died and 500 were injured in a triple train crash.	Immediate cause was a signal failure caused by a technician failing to isolate and remove a wire. Contributory causes included degradation of working practices, problems with training, testing quality and communications standards, poor supervision. Lessons not learnt from past incidents. No effective system for monitoring or limiting excessive working hours.
Herald of Free Enterprise *Transport sector* 1987	This roll-on roll-off ferry sank in shallow water off Zeebrugge killing 189 passengers and crew.	Immediate cause was the failure to close the bow doors before leaving port. No effective reporting system to check the bow doors. Formal inquiry reported that the company was 'infected with the disease of sloppiness'. Commercial pressures and friction between ship and shore management had led to safety lessons not being learnt.
Union Carbide Bhopal, India *Chemical processing* 1984	The plant released a cloud of toxic methyl isocynate. Death toll was 2500 and over one quarter of the city's population was affected by the gas.	The leak was caused by a discharge of water into a storage tank. This was the result of a combination of operator error, poor maintenance, failed safety systems and poor safety management.
Space Shuttle *Challenger* *Aerospace* 1986	An explosion shortly after lift-off killed all seven astronauts on board.	An O-ring seal on one of the solid rocket boosters split after take-off releasing a jet of ignited fuel. Inadequate response to internal warnings about the faulty seal design. Decision taken to go for launch in very cold temperature despite faulty seal. Decision-making result of conflicting scheduling/safety goals, mindset, and effects of fatigue.

Table 1 *Some illustrative major accidents (continued)*

Accident, industry and date	Consequences	Human contribution and other causes
Piper Alpha *Offshore* 1988	167 workers died in the North Sea after a major explosion and fire on an offshore platform.	Formal inquiry found a number of technical and organisational failures. Maintenance error that eventually led to the leak was the result of inexperience, poor maintenance procedures and poor learning by the organisation. There was a breakdown in communications and the permit-to-work system at shift changeover and safety procedures were not practised sufficiently.
Chernobyl *Nuclear industry* 1986	1000 MW Reactor exploded releasing radioactivity over much of Europe. Environmental and human cost.	Causes are much debated but Soviet investigative team admitted 'deliberate, systematic and numerous violations' of safety procedures by operators.
Texaco Refinery, Milford Haven *Chemical processing* 1994	An explosion on the site was followed by a major hydrocarbon fire and a number of secondary fires. There was severe damage to process plant, buildings and storage tanks. 26 people sustained injuries, none serious.	The incident was caused by flammable hydrocarbon liquid being continuously pumped into a process vessel that had its outlet closed. This was the result of a combination of: an erroneous control system reading of a valve state, modifications which had not been fully assessed, failure to provide operators with the necessary process overviews and attempts to keep the unit running when it should have been shut down.

It is all too easy to provide examples of accidents where 'human error' has given rise to a major accident with loss of life and injuries. Table 1 illustrates how the failure of people at many levels within an organisation can contribute to a major disaster. For many of these major accidents the human failure was not the sole cause but one of a number of causes, including technical and organisational failures, that led to the final outcome. Remember that many 'everyday' minor accidents and near misses also involve human failures.

We all make errors irrespective of how much training and experience we possess or how motivated we are to do it right. Failures are more serious for jobs where the consequences of errors are not protected. However, errors can occur in all tasks, not just those which are called safety-critical.

The human contribution to accidents

People can cause or contribute to accidents (or mitigate the consequences) in a number of ways:

- Through a failure a person can directly cause an accident. However, people tend not to make errors deliberately. We are often 'set up to fail' by the way our brain processes information, by our training, through the design of equipment and procedures and even through the culture of the organisation we work for.

- People can make disastrous decisions even when they are aware of the risks. We can also misinterpret a situation and act inappropriately as a result. Both of these can lead to the escalation of an incident.

- On the other hand we can intervene to stop potential accidents. Many companies have their own anecdotes about recovery from a potential incident through the timely actions of individuals. Mitigation of the possible effects of an incident can result from human resourcefulness and ingenuity.

- The degree of loss of life can be reduced by the emergency response of operators and crew. Emergency planning and response including appropriate training can significantly improve rescue situations.

The consequences of human failures can be immediate or delayed.

Active failures have an immediate consequence and are usually made by front-line people such as drivers, control room staff or machine operators. In a situation where there is no room for error these active failures have an immediate impact on health and safety.

Latent failures are made by people whose tasks are removed in time and space from operational activities, eg designers, decision makers and managers. Latent failures are typically failures in health and safety management systems (design, implementation or monitoring). Examples of latent failures are:

- poor design of plant and equipment;
- ineffective training;
- inadequate supervision;
- ineffective communications; and
- uncertainties in roles and responsibilities.

Latent failures provide as great, if not a greater, potential danger to health and safety as active failures. Latent failures are usually hidden within an organisation until they are triggered by an event likely to have serious consequences.

Investigating the causes of accidents

After an accident involving human failure there may be an investigation into the causes and contributing factors. Very often, little attempt is made to understand *why* the human failures occurred. However, finding out both the immediate and the underlying causes of an accident is the key to preventing similar accidents through the design of effective control measures. Typical examples of immediate causes and contributing factors for human failures are given in Box C. This is not a complete list and you will be able to add other causes. The HSE publication *Successful health and safety management*[1] gives more information on investigating accidents. Formal methods for causal analysis exist and are described in CCPS (1994).[2]

Job factors

- illogical design of equipment and instruments
- constant disturbances and interruptions
- missing or unclear instructions
- poorly maintained equipment
- high workload
- noisy and unpleasant working conditions

Individual factors

- low skill and competence levels
- tired staff
- bored or disheartened staff
- individual medical problems

Organisation and management factors

- poor work planning, leading to high work pressure
- lack of safety systems and barriers
- inadequate responses to previous incidents
- management based on one-way communications
- deficient co-ordination and responsibilities
- poor management of health and safety
- poor health and safety culture

BOX C *Examples of often cited causes of human failures in accidents*

Causes of human failure

There are different types of human failures: **errors** and **violations** (see Figure 2)

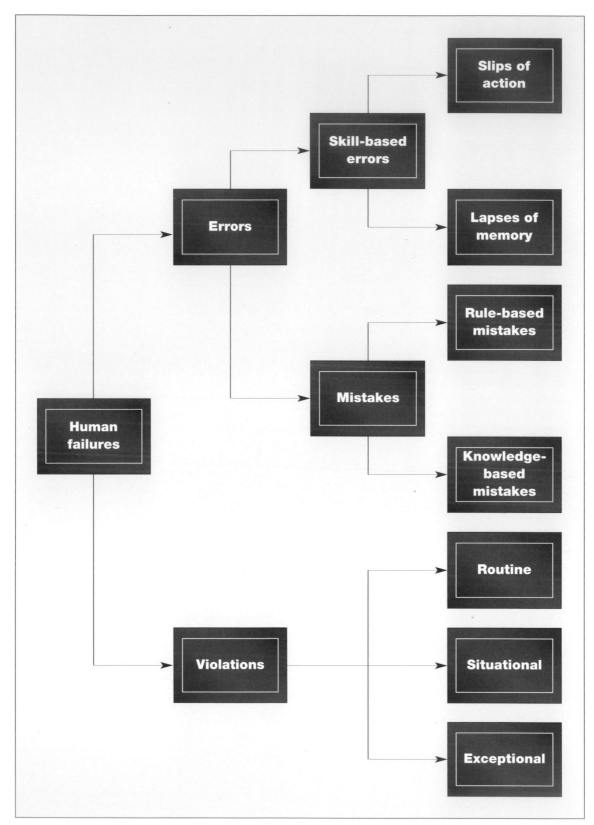

Figure 2 *Types of human failure*

■ a **human error** is an action or decision which was *not intended*, which involved a deviation from an accepted standard, and which led to an undesirable outcome.

■ a **violation** is a *deliberate* deviation from a rule or procedure. Violations are discussed in detail in the section on 'Breaking the rules', page 16.

Errors fall into three categories: **slips**, **lapses** and **mistakes**.

Slips and lapses occur in very familiar tasks which we can carry out without much need for conscious attention. These tasks are called 'skill-based' and are very vulnerable to errors if our attention is diverted, even momentarily. Driving a car is a typical skill-based task for many of us. Slips and lapses are the errors which are made by even the most experienced, well-trained and highly-motivated people. They often result in omitted steps in repair, maintenance, calibration or testing tasks. We need to be aware of these types of errors and try to design equipment and tasks to avoid or reduce their occurrence. We can also try to increase the opportunities to detect and correct such errors. It can be useful to make everyone aware that slips and lapses exist and to consider them during accident investigation.

Slips are failures in carrying out the actions of a task. They are described as 'actions-not-as-planned'. Examples would be: picking up the wrong component from a mixed box, operating the wrong switch, transposing digits when copying out numbers and misordering steps in a procedure. Typical slips might include:

■ performing an action too soon in a procedure or leaving it too late;
■ omitting a step or series of steps from a task;
■ carrying out an action with too much or too little strength (eg over-torquing a bolt);
■ performing the action in the wrong direction (eg turning a control knob to the right rather than the left, or moving a switch up rather than down);
■ doing the right thing but on the wrong object (eg switching the wrong switch); and
■ carrying out the wrong check but on the right item (eg checking a dial but for the wrong value).

The following is an example of a slip causing an accident:

Two similarly named chemicals were manufactured at a chemical works in batch reactions. Each required the presence of an inorganic base to maintain alkalinity to prevent exothermic side reactions. Development work was in progress which involved altering the various ratios of chemicals in each reaction. A chemist, in calculating the quantities of inorganic base required, inadvertently transposed the figures (a typical slip). As a result one reaction was carried out with only 70% of the required base present and an exothermic side reaction resulted. The subsequent explosion destroyed the plant. The system was not designed to cope with a runaway exothermic reaction. There was no system for checking the calculations.

Box D *An example of a slip causing an accident*

Lapses cause us to forget to carry out an action, to lose our place in a task or even to forget what we had intended to do. They can be reduced by minimising distractions and interruptions to tasks and by providing effective reminders especially for tasks which take some time to complete or involve periods of waiting. A useful reminder could be as simple as a partially completed checklist placed in a clearly visible location for the person doing the task. We may be able to eliminate some of these lapses through better design of equipment or tasks, as in Box E.

> An experienced road tanker driver had virtually completed the filling of his vehicle from a bulk tank of flammable liquid when a nearby telephone rang. After ignoring it for some five minutes he closed the various valves on the installation and went to answer it. On returning to the vehicle he drove away having forgotten that he had not disconnected the tanker hose from the installation. Fixed pipework from the installation fractured and approximately one tonne of material was lost. The installation was not fitted with a drive-away protection device.

Box E *An example of a worker being distracted*

Mistakes are a more complex type of human error where we do the wrong thing believing it to be right. The failure involves our mental processes which control how we plan, assess information, make intentions and judge consequences. Two types of mistakes exist, rule-based and knowledge-based.

Rule-based mistakes occur when our behaviour is based on remembered rules or familiar procedures. We have a strong tendency to use familiar rules or solutions even when these are not the most convenient or efficient.

> An operator was very familiar with the task of filling a tank. He expected the filling procedure to take about 30 minutes. However, on this occasion the diameter of the pipe entering the tank had been enlarged and the tank was filling much more rapidly than he anticipated. He ignored the high level alarms on the grounds that the tank could not be full so quickly. The tank overflowed. Improved communications would have alerted the operator to the changes that had been made to the pipe.

Box F *An example of a rule-based mistake*

In unfamiliar circumstances we have to revert to consciously making goals, developing plans and procedures. Planning or problem solving needs us to reason from first principles or use analogies. Misdiagnoses and miscalculations can result when we use this **knowledge-based reasoning**, as in Box G.

> The investigation following a major collapse of a tunnel found that the organisation had relied on the experience of one person as a control measure. However, the nature of the method of working meant that this person had no reliable instrumentation for detecting when the tunnel was becoming unstable. Relying on 'experience' was actually relying on knowledge-based reasoning of the 'expert' and was not an effective control method to prevent a serious collapse given the unpredictable nature of the event. The expert needed more reliable instruments to carry out this work.

Box G *An example of relying on 'experience'*

Inexperience and lack of information

The kinds of error described above typically occur with people who are experienced and trained.
It is important to remember that human errors often occur if a person is not experienced or does not receive the correct information such as knowledge of potential hazards. The following example shows this.

> A man was killed while removing the lid of a 45 gallon drum using a burning torch. He had not been told that the drum contained flammable residues. The drum exploded when heat was applied.

Box H *An example of incomplete information*

Lack of understanding often arises through a failure to communicate effectively. Shift handovers are a particularly vulnerable time for communication failures as is shown by this next example (see Chapter 4 for more information).

> Contamination of a beach near a nuclear reprocessing plant occurred partly from a failure in communications between two shifts. One shift presumed that a particular tank only contained aqueous layers, when in fact it also contained floating radioactive solids which they presumed had been removed earlier. The result was that these solids were inadvertently pumped to the sea tanks along with the aqueous layer.

Box I *An example of a failure to communicate*

Reducing errors

Errors are more likely to occur under certain circumstances including:

■ work environment stressors, eg extremes of heat, humidity, noise, vibration, poor lighting, restricted workspace;

■ extreme task demands, eg high workload, tasks demanding high levels of alertness, jobs which are very monotonous and repetitive, situations with many distractions and interruptions;

■ social and organisational stressors, eg insufficient staffing levels, inflexible or overdemanding work schedules, conflicts with work colleagues, peer pressure and conflicting attitudes to health and safety;

■ individual stressors, eg inadequate training and experience, high levels of fatigue, reduced alertness, family problems, ill-health, misuse of alcohol and drugs; and

■ equipment stressors, eg poorly designed displays and controls, inaccurate and confusing instructions and procedures.

Error control and reduction needs to consider these influences on peoples' behaviour and performance. Steps to reduce human errors include:

■ addressing the conditions and reducing the stressors which increase the frequency of errors;

■ designing plant and equipment to prevent slips and lapses occurring or to increase the chance of detecting and correcting them;

■ making certain that arrangements for training are effective;

■ designing jobs to avoid the need for tasks which involve very complex decisions, diagnoses or calculations, eg by writing procedures for rare events requiring decisions and actions;

- ensuring proper supervision particularly for inexperienced staff, or for tasks where there is a need for independent checking;
- checking that job aids such as procedures and instructions are clear, concise, available, up-to-date and accepted by users;
- considering the possibility of human error when undertaking risk assessments;
- thinking about the different causes of human errors during incident investigations in order to introduce measures to reduce the risk of a repeat incident; and
- monitoring that measures taken to reduce error are effective.

Breaking the rules

Violations are any deliberate deviations from rules, procedures, instructions and regulations. The breaching or violating of health and safety rules or procedures is a significant cause of many accidents and injuries at work. Removing the guard on dangerous machinery or driving too fast will clearly increase the risk of an accident. Health risks are also increased by rule breaking. For example a worker in a noisy workplace who breaks the site rules about wearing ear defenders increases their risk of occupational deafness. Our knowledge of why people break rules can help us to assess the potential risks from violations and to develop control strategies to manage these risks effectively.

In the workplace rules are broken for many different reasons. Most violations are motivated by a desire to carry out the job despite the prevailing constraints, goals and expectations. Very rarely are they wilful acts of sabotage or vandalism. Violations are divided into three categories: **routine, situational** and **exceptional**.

With a **routine violation**, breaking the rule or procedure has become a normal way of working within the work group. This can be due to:

- the desire to cut corners to save time and energy;
- the perception that the rules are too restrictive;
- the belief that the rules no longer apply;
- lack of enforcement of the rule; and
- new workers starting a job where routine violations are the norm and not realising that this is not the correct way of working.

Here are some examples of routine violations (taken from HFRG 1995).[3]

> The inquiry into the Clapham Rail Crash found that maintenance working practices had degraded to the point where it had become routine not to use the prescribed method for certain tasks. Poor supervision and problems with training and testing meant that this situation was allowed to persist.

> In a study of Dutch railways, 80% of the workforce considered that the rules were mainly concerned with pinning blame, while 95% thought that work could not be finished on time if all the rules were followed.

Box J *Examples of routine violations of rules*

To reduce routine violations managers could:

- take steps to increase the chances of violations being detected, eg by routine monitoring;
- think about whether there are any unnecessary rules;
- make rules and procedures relevant and practical;
- explain the reasons behind certain rules or procedures and their relevance;
- improve design factors that affect the likelihood of corner cutting (see Box K); and
- involve the workforce in drawing up rules to try to increase acceptance.

- Awkward, uncomfortable or painful working posture
- Excessively awkward, tiring or slow controls or equipment
- Difficulty in getting in or out of operating or maintenance position
- Equipment or software which seems unduly slow to respond
- High noise levels which prevent clear communication
- Frequent false alarms from instrumentation
- Instrumentation perceived to be unreliable
- Procedures which are hard to read or out of date
- Difficult-to-use or uncomfortable personal protective equipment
- Unpleasant environments, eg dust, fumes, extreme heat or cold

BOX K *Design features which increase violations*

In the case of **situational violations** breaking the rule is due to pressures from the job such as being under time pressure, insufficient staff for the workload, the right equipment not being available, or even extreme weather conditions. It may be very difficult to comply with the rule in a particular situation or staff may think that the rule is unsafe under the circumstances. Risk assessments may help to identify the potential for such violations. Encouraging reporting of job pressures through open communication will also be helpful.

A steel erector was killed when he fell 20 m from a structure under erection. Although harnesses were provided there was no provision for fixing them and there were no other safeguards available.

Box L *An example of a situational violation*

To reduce these situational violations managers need to consider:

- improving the working environment;
- providing appropriate supervision;
- improving job design and planning; and
- establishing a positive health and safety culture.

Exceptional violations rarely happen and only then when something has gone wrong. To solve a new problem you feel you need to break a rule even though you are aware that you will be 'taking a risk'. You believe, falsely, that the benefits outweigh the risks. For example:

Before the accident at the Chernobyl nuclear power plant a series of tests were being undertaken. When an operator failure led to dangerously low power levels the test should have been abandoned. Operators and engineers continued to improvise in an unfamiliar and increasingly unstable regime to protect the test plan.

Box L *An example of an exceptional violation*

To minimise exceptional violations:

■ provide more training for abnormal and emergency situations;

■ during risk assessments think about the possibility of violations; and

■ try to reduce the time pressure on staff to act quickly in novel situations.

Organisational and managerial role in violations

Organisational culture and managerial goals and priorities can influence whether health and safety rules are broken. If the wrong messages about health and safety are received rule breaking can be encouraged. A lack of visible communication from management can be seen as somehow condoning violations of health and safety rules. Managers and supervisors need to send positive messages about health and safety. Further information on these issues is given in HSG65[1] and in other parts of this guidance.

RELATED CASE STUDIES

Relevant case studies on violations in Chapter 6 include F *Lighting underground locomotive cabs safely* which gives an example of how a problem with drivers violating speed rules was investigated and resolved. Case study N *Introduction of a mini-crane in a chemical plant* may also provide useful tips.

KEY MESSAGES

Everyone can make errors no matter how well trained and motivated they are. Sometimes we are 'set up' by the system to fail. The challenge is to develop error-tolerant systems and to prevent errors from occurring.

Failures arising from people other than those directly involved in operational or maintenance activities are important. Managers' and designers' failures may lie hidden until they are triggered at some time in the future.

There are two main types of human failure: errors and violations. Controls will be more effective if the types are identified and addressed separately.

Reducing human error involves far more than taking disciplinary action against an individual. There are a range of measures which are more effective controls including design of the job and equipment, procedures, and training.

Paying attention to individual attitudes and motivations, design features of the job and the organisation will help to reduce violations.

CHAPTER THREE

Designing for people

Many of the human factors problems highlighted so far in this guidance can be prevented or reduced during design. This chapter introduces the following topics:

- some basic principles of ergonomic design;
- job design to improve levels of job satisfaction and mental well-being;
- writing procedures which are more likely to be used efficiently;
- designing warnings that are more effective; and
- assessing human reliability.

Ergonomic design

Ergonomics is about ensuring a good 'fit' between people and the things they use. People vary enormously in height and weight, in physical strength, in ability to handle information and in many other ways. Ergonomics uses information about human abilities, attributes and limitations to ensure that our equipment, work and workplaces allow for such variations. For example, a car built for only 'average' sized drivers might require larger people to crouch, while smaller people may be unable to reach the pedals. This is clearly unacceptable, so designers use information about variations in size, reach and so on to produce cars that most people can operate comfortably; conveniently and safely.

Designing tasks, equipment and workstations to suit the user can reduce human error, accidents and ill health. Failure to observe ergonomic principles can have serious consequences for individuals and for the whole organisation. Effective use of ergonomics will make work safer, healthier and more productive.

Knowing that you have an ergonomic problem

If you look at the circumstances surrounding incidents and near misses in your workplace you may find problems such as people being:

- unable to see important displays;

- unable to reach controls;
- unable to work in a comfortable position;
- overloaded with too much information at one time; and
- inattentive because there is too little to do.

The people who do a particular job are in a good position to identify especially awkward or difficult tasks. Remember that they may also have become used to a poor design. Some jobs may be extremely tiring or liable to cause aches and pains. Observation of how people actually use equipment can highlight ergonomic problems. Makeshift adaptations to machines such as lengthened levers, extra labels on switches, blocks of wood or cushions used to alter working positions, can be a sign that the design of the equipment or the job needs attention.

Medical and sickness absence records may reveal patterns of injury or complaint that could be associated with particular jobs.

Table 2 lists some questions that you can use to identify possible mismatches between the abilities and physical attributes of people and the demands of the equipment they work with.

Table 2 *Is the task and equipment ergonomically satisfactory?*

Consider all the ways and circumstances in which the equipment or system may be used.
<ul><li>Does it suit your body size?</li><li>Does it also suit all other users?</li><li>Can you see and hear all you need to readily?</li><li>Do you understand all the information that is presented?</li><li>Do errors occur frequently and are they easy to detect and put right?</li><li>Does the equipment or system cause discomfort if you use it for any length of time?</li><li>Is it convenient to use?</li><li>Is it easy to learn how to use?</li><li>Is it compatible with other systems in use?</li><li>Are you forced to make movements which feel too fast or too slow?</li><li>Can you reach the controls that you use frequently without overstretching and without adopting an awkward posture?</li><li>Can you move safely and with ease between operating positions?</li><li>Is the workplace environment comfortable for you?</li><li>Do you feel stressed physically (through noise, temperature, pacing of the machine, etc) or psychologically (from deadlines, workrate, etc)?</li><li>Could any of these aspects be improved?</li><li>Do other users have similar reactions?</li></ul>

Problems which ergonomics can address

Good ergonomic design can help with a range of problems. Some of the most obvious are to do with body size; eg work surfaces that are uncomfortable to sit at because they don't allow sufficient clearance for users' legs.

The layout of controls and displays can influence the safety of a system. Typical problems include:

■ switches which can be inadvertently knocked on or off;

■ control panel layouts which are difficult to understand;

■ displays which force the user to bend or stretch to read them properly;

■ critical displays which are not in the operator's normal field of view;

■ poorly identified controls which the operator could select by mistake; and

■ emergency stop buttons which are difficult to reach.

Table 3 lists some factors which are important in the ergonomic design of controls.

Table 3 *Ergonomic design of controls*

Consider these aspects of the design of controls:
■ Size (relative to force required)
■ Weight (relative to user's position)
■ Resistance (to prevent accidental use)
■ Feedback (to user's senses)
■ Texture (slip, grip, glare issues)
■ Coding by colour (differences need to be visible to user)
■ Coding by shape (simple forms are easier to identify between)
■ Coding by texture
■ Coding by size
■ Location
■ Compatibility (between displays and controls)
■ Stereotypes (usual way of operating, eg switching a control on by pressing down)

Taking action

If you find an ergonomic problem, a minor alteration may be all that is necessary to make a task easier and safer to perform. For instance, height-adjustable chairs allow individual users to work at their preferred work height, platforms may help operators to reach badly located controls (but beware of allowing access to danger points). If shadows or overall lighting levels are a problem, local lighting for particular tasks may be an easily adopted solution.

Always make sure that any alterations are evaluated by the people who do the job and take care that a change introduced to solve one problem does not cause difficulties somewhere else (eg for maintenance staff).

Where a straightforward solution does not seem possible and more complex redesign is indicated you need to consult a trained ergonomist. A list of professional societies is given at the end of this guidance.

RELATED CASE STUDIES

A number of case studies illustrating ergonomic problems and their solutions are given in Chapter 6. Look in particular at cases A, C, E, G, I, J, M, N and Q. Cases A, N and Q show how involving users can improve the acceptance of, and commitment to, any changes.

Designing jobs for mental well-being

Problems with mental well-being are one of the major causes of time off work. Depression and anxiety stem from causes both outside and inside work. They affect not only the mental well-being of staff but also organisational performance through increased staff turnover, poor work performance and accidents at work.

When jobs are designed it tends to be the technology or the equipment which determines the content of the job. However, it is also desirable to design jobs in ways which improve levels of job satisfaction for the workforce. Feeling satisfied with your job has been shown to improve your performance at work, reduce your feelings of being under stress, and generally lead to a sense of mental well-being.

Sources of stress

HSE[4] defines stress as 'the reaction that people have to excessive pressure or other types of demands placed upon them. It arises when they worry that they can't cope'. A number of sources of stress have been identified and are shown in Figure 3. They include:

■ Factors intrinsic to the job, eg poor physical working conditions (such as high levels of noise, poor ventilation), working inconvenient and excessive hours, working on a repetitive and fast-paced task, or having a job which involves risk or danger. The introduction of new technology can be another source of stress. Both work overload (having too much to do or the work being too difficult) and work underload (routine, boring and under-stimulating tasks) can be sources of stress.

■ If a person's role in an organisation is ambiguous, ie they do not have a clear idea of their role and responsibilities or their work objectives, this can be a source of stress. Role conflict and conflict situations are possible sources of stress, eg being torn between competing or conflicting job demands or having to perform tasks that you do not like or which are outside your job specification. Having responsibility at work for other people can be particularly stressful.

■ Other people at work and our interactions with them can be sources of both support and stress. Relationships with our bosses, our subordinates and our co-workers are all important. Mistrust of co-workers and poor communications with them can lead to low job satisfaction. Close supervision and a management style characterised by constant negative performance feedback is related to high levels of stress and poor worker health. (Organisational culture is discussed in Chapter 4.)

■   A lack of job security, fear of redundancy, or forced early retirement are potential stressors relating to career development. Another source of job dissatisfaction would be under or over-promotion arising from a failure to advance or promotion to a position beyond one's capabilities. A particular stressor in some jobs is the threat of violence in the workplace and the experience of trauma following a violent incident.

■   People can sometimes feel they do not belong to an organisation or lack opportunities to participate. If the workforce is allowed more participation in decision making this can lead to higher levels of job satisfaction and lower absenteeism and staff turnover. Participation in the decision-making process may create a sense of belonging and can improve communication channels within the company. It can generate a sense of 'being in control' which is important for mental well-being.

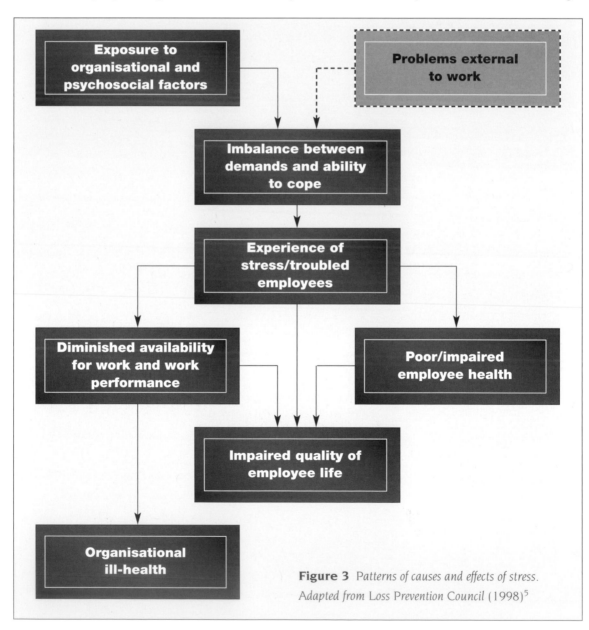

Figure 3 *Patterns of causes and effects of stress. Adapted from Loss Prevention Council (1998)[5]*

Individual differences

Different people will react in different ways to the same situation. Individual characteristics (such as attitudes, abilities, and personality) will interact with features of the job and organisation (eg job characteristics, work environment and health and safety culture) to affect a person's sense of well-being and job satisfaction. The degree of fit between the person and the job can significantly influence their sense of mental well-being. There will be variations between people in which jobs will promote job satisfaction or job dissatisfaction. This needs to be taken into account in the design of tasks. For example, the effects of a repetitive, monotonous task are worse if the work is also machine rather than self-paced. However, a proportion of workers do prefer machine to self-paced work. In general though machine-paced work is often combined with repetitiveness, physical constraint and under-utilisation of skills and associated with a higher level of stress.

Improving job design

When thinking about improving job satisfaction and reducing stress levels organisations often focus on the individual worker through the provision of stress management courses and employee assistance programmes. Although helpful, attempts to deal with difficulties on an individual basis are ultimately only 'sticking plasters' and the problems will tend to recur. Another complementary approach is to consider organisational and job design. Solutions here will in the long run be more cost effective as the underlying work-related causes will be identified and resolved.

Throughout this century jobs have tended to become increasingly monotonous and controlled. Many jobs are designed to minimise skill requirements, maximise management control and minimise the time required to perform a task. Jobs designed like this have a human cost in terms of negative attitudes to the job and poor mental and physical health and attempts have been made to redesign such work to improve the quality of working life. Such redesign is based on increasing one or more of the following job characteristics:

- variety of tasks or skills (increased use of capabilities);
- autonomy (higher control over when and how tasks are done);
- completeness (whether a job produces an identifiable end result which makes the task more significant and meaningful for the worker); and
- feedback from the job (improved knowledge of the results of the work activities).

Other characteristics of work which are also thought to be important for job satisfaction are the amount and quality of social interaction with co-workers, responsibility for technology and output, and the mental demands of a job including the need to pay close, constant attention to a task and the need to diagnose and solve problems.

Typical ways of work redesign are:

Job rotation. Here people rotate through a small number of different but typically similar jobs. The rotation is often frequent, eg weekly. This can increase task variety but as it does not improve other job factors it is of limited value in improving job satisfaction. The company benefits by having more people who can carry out a particular job. Effective task training is needed especially if a job requires a high degree of skill or if there is the potential for an error with serious consequences.

Horizontal job enlargement. A person's job is altered to include additional tasks which are similar to those which are already being carried out. Many companies now encourage staff to become multi-skilled. Job enlargement does increase the variety of work but it may not necessarily improve job satisfaction. At worse it can result in the aggregation of several equally boring and stressful tasks.

Vertical job enlargement. The redesign of a job to include additional decision-making responsibilities and/or higher-level challenging tasks. This increases autonomy and variety.

Job enrichment. This is similar to vertical job enlargement but builds into jobs greater scope for personal achievement and recognition, more challenging and responsible work and more opportunity for advancement and growth. Elements can include feedback about performance, more control over resources and increased participation in decision making.

Autonomous work groups. The aim here is to provide a job which is complete; the group sees it through from start to finish and has the responsibility for planning, co-ordinating and evaluating its own work activities. This can lead to improvements in product quality and quantity. There can be problems if wage levels are dependent on the speed with which items are produced. If so, pressure may be put on slower members of a group. There can be strong motivation within a work group to attain goals. This may lead to very high levels of effort and a negative impact on the mental and physical health of group members.

Employee involvement and participation. Involvement and participation of staff in job, task and equipment design and redesign is an important tool in the reduction of both stress levels and safety risks. Individuals are often able to identify and propose solutions to some of the ergonomic problems in their workplace as is shown in many of the case studies in this guidance. However, such initiatives need to have the support of management to make them work. Extended use of participation can create raised expectations for employees which may be difficult to meet. Employee involvement can appear threatening to managers who are used to making their own decisions.

Job redesign usually has a positive impact on job satisfaction, motivation, employee mental health and performance as long as it is not restricted to just increasing job variety. Such redesign usually occurs in combination with other changes such as staffing levels, pay rates, or management style which are likely to also affect these outcomes.

> ### RELATED CASE STUDIES.
>
> Case studies K, O and P look at instances where stress and/or job satisfaction were problems for the organisation. Case studies which show how involving employees was helpful are A, B, D, N and Q.

Writing procedures

Procedures, especially operating and maintenance procedures, are important for the prevention of accidents and ill health. Written procedures are vital in maintaining consistency and in ensuring that everyone has the same basic level of information. They are a key element of a safety management system and an important training tool. However, poor procedures can be a reason for people not following recommended actions.

As well as being technically accurate, procedures need to be well-written, usable and up to date. Remember that even if your procedures are not formally written down they exist through the working practices of staff. Ask yourself:

- Are your procedures accessible?
- Are they actually followed by staff?
- Are they written so that they can be understood and followed easily?
- Do they reflect the tasks as they are actually carried out?
- Do the procedures include key safety information?
- Are they kept up to date and reviewed occasionally?

Procedures ideally need to:

- be accurate and complete;
- be clear and concise with an appropriate level of detail;
- be current and up to date;
- be supported by training;
- identify any hazards;
- state necessary precautions for hazards;
- use familiar language;
- use consistent terminology;
- reflect how tasks are actually carried out;
- promote ownership by users;
- be in a suitable format; and
- be accessible.

Writing better procedures

Start by collecting information about the task and the users. To do this you could carry out an activity analysis (see Chapter 5 for details). You will also need to have the results of any relevant risk assessments to hand so that the procedure can reflect arrangements to maintain adequate control of identified risks. Here are some issues to think about:

- consider both the difficulty and importance of the task(s) to be documented;
- find out how often the task is carried out and the potential hazards;
- think about who will use the procedure and the level of information they need (providing too much information may lead to less use of the procedure if users find it too detailed and hard to follow, too little information may mean that an inexperienced person will not be able to carry out the task);
- establish the skills, experience level, past training and needs of the users of the procedure; and
- look at whether the procedure needs to be supported by training in order to promote understanding and effective use.

Try to **promote ownership** by encouraging users to participate in the preparation and maintenance of the procedure. For example experienced staff could write the procedure and users could review it. Ask users about the ease of use of a procedure and whether it is easy to understand. Encourage users to suggest improvements to existing procedures.

Procedures can appear in many **different forms**, eg as printed text documents, electronically, as quick reference cards, or as posted notices. It is important that users know where the procedures can be found and that this is convenient for them. If it takes too long to find a procedure users will be more reluctant to use it. Procedures which are duplicated, eg as posted notices as well as printed text documents, should not contain conflicting instructions.

Think about the issue of **style**. As general guidance keep sentences short and avoid use of complex sentence structure. This will make the procedure easier to read and understand. Try to write the required actions that users need to do in positive active sentences eg 'Open valve A then valve B'. This is easier to follow than the more complicated - 'After opening valve B open valve A' or 'Do not open valve B until valve A has been opened'.

Put items in the order in which they need to be carried out. It is easier to follow a procedure which states 'Do A then do B' rather than 'Before doing B do A'. For procedures which are complex, rarely carried out, or performed in adverse conditions it is helpful to document the steps of the procedure one at a time.

Effective use can be made of:

- flow charts;
- decision tables (often in the form of 'if condition X, then go to step Y');
- questions (eg 'is the temperature greater than $100°$ C? Yes, go to step 1; No, go to step 2'); and
- diagrams.

Divide longer procedures into shorter chunks. This helps users to go back to a particular step if they are interrupted or if the task takes some time to carry out.

AVOID USING ALL CAPITAL LETTERS FOR THE TEXT. Research shows that this is slower and more difficult for us to read than the lower case text we are more used to. Decide how features such as capitals, bold, italics, and underlining will be used. Overuse of these features is very distracting for users.

Avoid using very small fonts (eg 8 point or smaller) as this is very difficult for users to read.

Make good use of open space in the printed text. If the page appears too cluttered, users will be discouraged from reading it. Although the procedure may have more pages, providing spaces between steps on the page will make it more usable.

Try to use the same **format** for all procedures. This will help users find their way around the text.

An inconsistent format could confuse the user. A typical format would include:

■ purpose of the procedure;
■ precautions which must be observed to avoid potential hazards;
■ special tools or equipment needed;
■ initial conditions which must be satisfied before starting;
■ references to other relevant documents, eg data sheets or manuals; and
■ procedural steps to perform the task safely and efficiently.

Users may be very familiar with some frequently carried out procedures. Here it may be more effective if the procedure is in the form of a quick reference card containing the key precautions and action steps.

Warning information about potential hazards is usually given in a precautions section at the start of the procedure and in the form of 'cautions' embedded in the procedural steps.

The precautions section needs to give the user information on what can happen, why, and the consequences of ignoring the precaution. It is best to restrict the precautions section to important health and safety issues. Too much information about self-evident issues will reduce the impact of the key messages.

Cautions in the procedural steps reiterate the precautions. Make sure that a caution appears immediately before the relevant step in the procedure and on the same page as the step. Ensure that the caution is clear, concise and contains only the relevant information for the user. Usually a caution or warning contains only information to alert or explain something to the user. Information about actions to carry out are contained in the procedural steps.

Designing warnings for maximum effect

In our working lives we are used to seeing written warnings, hearing alarms, and noticing warning signs or labels on products. All of these are intended to communicate risk to us. Yet, as accidents show, all too often we ignore these warnings. We need to ensure that warnings are effective, or consider alternative ways of reducing the risks.

Responding to warnings is important in all work situations but particularly so where the risks have not been completely eliminated through design. Here human actions may be needed to minimise risks. For example, control room staff need to respond to alarms to safeguard the plant and its process, medical staff need to respond to intensive care equipment alarms.

Risk assessments should indicate where it is important or essential for someone to respond appropriately to a warning or alarm.

Why have warnings?
Warnings serve three purposes:

■ alerting someone that a product or situation is hazardous;

■ specifying the potential seriousness of the hazard and the consequences of wrong action; and

■ specifying the preventive actions to be taken.

Do we comply with warnings?

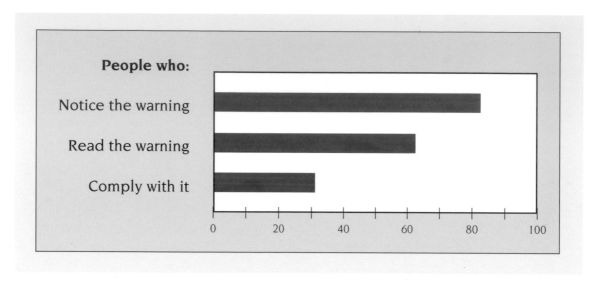

Figure 4 *Complying with written warnings*

As can be seen in Figure 4, while most people will notice a written warning, only half will actually read it and only a third will comply with the instructions. This shows that we cannot rely on a warning to produce the response we want.

People who comply most with warnings tend to:

■ perceive the risks of not complying to be *serious* or *highly likely* to occur;
■ believe they will be personally affected by the consequences;
■ are unfamiliar with the product or situation;
■ see other people around them are complying with the warnings;
■ find it is easy to comply, eg any necessary personal protection is close at hand; and
■ believe that if they comply there will be a real personal benefit.

What about the design of warnings?
Warnings should be conspicuous! Good design can help to make written warnings attention-grabbing. Use size, colour and pictures to make written warnings more visible. Take care if using pictorial symbols as these can be misunderstood or may deter further reading of the warning. The content of the warning should be brief, include only the relevant information and be easy to understand. It must be reasonable to carry out the instructions in a reliable and timely manner.

The instructions should specify what actions to take as well as which to avoid. It makes sense to place a warning where it is needed. A warning can be effective if placed at the beginning of instructions or embedded within them.

If the warning is spoken think about the pitch and stress of the voice delivering the message. Female voices tend to attract attention more readily than male voices. Consider not only the volume of a spoken message but also its audibility and whether it can be understood.

For other audible warnings the perceived urgency of the warning can be altered using changes in volume, pitch and repetition. Loud sounds of high pitch, sounds with rising tones and frequent repetitive sounds are usually seen as needing urgent action. In abnormal situations and emergencies (eg in control rooms or intensive care wards) staff often need to discriminate rapidly between many simultaneous audible alarms in order to identify the most urgent, so take care not to use such alerting features for low priority alarms.

Can warning response be improved?
Yes. Think about the people and the warning. People need to:

- be alert and sober;
- be seeking information (either because they suspect a hazard is present or because their past experience indicates that such information may be needed);
- accept the warning as being important (they should not be overloaded with information or other warnings and not have experienced many false alarms);
- believe the warning, receive information that is consistent with their past experience, accept the source of the warning as credible and see that other people are acting consistently with the warning;
- judge the risk to be significant (see the health and safety consequences as highly likely or severe, believe that they do not have control over the hazard, appreciate that the risks outweigh any adverse peer pressure and accept that the risks outweigh the cost/effort of avoidance);
- be capable of carrying out the required action; and
- remember how and when to carry out the action.

The warning needs to:

- be present when and where needed;
- give only the information needed; and
- be in a suitable format (brief, understandable and attention-grabbing).

Human Reliability Assessment

Human reliability is the opposite of human error. It is the probability of successfully performing a task. The reliability of a system depends on hardware, software and human reliability. It is important to be able to assess human reliability, particularly in a complex high-hazard system. Human Reliability Assessment (HRA) is a structured and systematic way of estimating the probability of human errors in specific tasks.

HRA is used in the nuclear, offshore and chemical processing industries as part of the risk assessment process. The overall method is generally applicable and can be used in other industrial sectors. There are three main reasons for the use of HRA:

- to give a benchmark for safety cases and design briefs;
- to enable comparison of alternative designs or organisational solutions; and
- to identify the weaker human links in a system so that appropriate control measures can be introduced.

A HRA is usually carried out by a trained risk assessor or a human reliability analyst. Representatives of the workforce need to be involved in the process to contribute specific task knowledge and experience. Differences between assessors can occur and, for tasks where human reliability is critical, independent assessments are useful. Analysts should be trained to increase their awareness of possible human errors, improve familiarity with data values and with available quantification methods. Feedback to assessors can help to improve their accuracy.

Steps in a Human Reliability Assessment
The following steps are usually part of a HRA.

Determine scope of assessment. The assessor will consider such issues as:

- Is the HRA part of a wider assessment?
- Is estimation of human error probabilities needed?
- What criteria are to be applied, eg fatalities, injuries?
- What resources and expertise are available?

Gather information. Collect information on which tasks need analysis. Visit the workplace and walk-through or talk-through these tasks.

Describe the tasks. Select a method to formally describe each task in terms of its goals, steps and the interactions between the person and the system. This establishes exactly what the person needs to do to carry out the task correctly.

Identify any human errors. Try to identify all the significant human errors that the person could make. Think about:

- What human errors can occur with each task? Formal methods exist to help with the identification of errors (see Kirwan).[6]
- What influences are there on performance? Typical influences include: time pressure, design of controls, displays and procedures, training and experience, fatigue, and levels of supervision.
- What are the consequences of the identified errors? Which are the significant errors?
- Are there any opportunities for detecting each error and recovering it?
- Are there any dependencies between the identified errors, eg might one person make the same error on more than one item of equipment? A typical example might be an operator miscalibrating more than one instrument because they have made a miscalculation.

Estimate human error probabilities. If required, estimate the human error probability for each significant error identified. This can be done using historical or field data if it is available or by asking knowledgeable experts for their judgement. Existing HRA methods may be used to estimate these probabilities (see Kirwan[6] or CCPS).[2] Combine individual error probabilities to give an overall Human Error Probability (HEP) for the task.

Give information to system analysts. Supply the information from the HRA to the system analysts and, if required, carry out further analyses.

Develop control measures. If the impact of human error on system reliability is significant then error reduction should follow. Control measures may include: redesign of the task or working environment, improvements to selection and training of staff, or placing additional barriers in the system to prevent the consequences of errors. For further information on control measures look at Chapter 2.

Estimation of Human Error Probabilities

The most debatable element of HRA lies with the estimation of Human Error Probabilities (HEPs). A variety of alternative methods are available for this task and are usually known by their acronyms such as THERP, HEART, SLIM, etc. Most of the methods involve some expert judgement but aim to reduce the biases inherent in such judgements. Typically the HRA method will provide a basic error rate for a task or individual error. This is then modified by considering plant or task specific factors such as supervision, time pressure, design of controls and displays.

The methods are more appropriate for those errors arising during the execution of a well-learned, familiar, routine task (so-called 'skill-based errors'). Take care when using the methods for other types of errors or for violations. It is important to understand the type of errors you are assessing and to make sure that the methods are appropriate.

You need to take care with the numbers generated by the methods. Do not assume that the results will be precise; instead treat the probabilities as estimates with a margin of error. If you need to consult a specialist, a list of professional societies is given at the end of this guidance.

KEY MESSAGES

Occupational ergonomics is about making a good 'fit' between people, the equipment they use, the task they carry out and the environment in which they work. Effective use of ergonomics will make work safer, healthier and more productive.

Jobs are often designed to minimise skill requirements and decision making. This can reduce levels of job satisfaction at work and can affect employee mental well-being. Job redesign usually has a positive impact on job satisfaction and mental well-being providing that it is not just the variety of tasks that is altered.

Consider the user when writing procedures. Use of procedures can be improved if human factors issues are addressed. Think carefully about the format, style and content

---

of procedures to make them easy to use and understand. Try to promote ownership of procedures through involvement of users in their development, review or updating.

Do not assume that everyone will notice, read and comply with warnings. To reduce risks consider additional controls. Think about the design, content and feasibility of a warning. Consider individual factors which are known to influence warning behaviour.

Human Reliability Assessment (HRA) is useful within the wider approach to occupational health and safety. It is a logical part of the process of risk assessment and is carried out in a stepwise manner. Training, auditing, feedback and independent analysis can all improve the HRA process and results.

CHAPTER FOUR

Managing the influences on human performance

In the last chapter we looked at how to improve human performance through the design of jobs, equipment, procedures and warnings. Here we consider some topics which influence people's performance and health and safety-related behaviour at work. These areas are among those which need to be actively managed by an organisation to control health and safety risks effectively. Four topics are covered:

- fatigue and shift work;
- communication;
- risk perception and the risk-taking behaviour of individuals; and
- the health and safety culture of an organisation.

Fatigue and shift work

Many individuals work shift systems, work at night, or work very extended hours. Such working patterns can lead to adverse effects upon health, particularly for night workers. Reduced levels of performance have been associated with night working which can also increase the likelihood of accidents and ill health.

Some people experience severe fatigue at work. This can lead to poorer performance on tasks which require attention, decision-making or high levels of skill. For safety-critical work the effects of fatigue can give rise to increased risks. However, all too often, fatigue is seen as a familiar and acceptable part of everyday life. Working long hours may even be accepted in the culture of a workplace as 'the thing to do'.

Some organisations are starting to look carefully at three aspects of shift work:

- risks to health;
- possible impact on safety; and
- effects on shift workers' social and family lives.

Health effects

Shift work, especially night work, can lead to the following health problems:

- Difficulty in falling asleep and staying asleep, difficulty in staying alert and awake at work, reduced quality and quantity of sleep, increased use of sleeping pills. There may be a gradual build-up of sleep loss into a 'sleep debt'.
- Gastrointestinal disorders. These may be linked to an increased tendency to eat snack meals at work.
- Respiratory problems. Asthma attacks may be worse at night. Allergic reactions may become worse. Lung function declines at night especially for those with chronic respiratory conditions.
- Individuals taking regular medication may have problems with shift work. Dosages may need to be altered to take account of variations of drug effectiveness due to the time of day.
- A proportion of people find that they cannot cope with working shifts. They may experience health problems which become acute only weeks after starting shift work and they may need to move to other duties.

Possible effects on safety

Job performance may be poorer on shift work especially when working night shifts. Tasks tend to be completed more slowly at night, although this can be balanced by altering the workload. In general the early hours of the morning, eg between 02.00 and 05.00 present the highest risk for fatigue-related accidents.

Sleep loss can lead to lowered levels of alertness. Cumulative sleep loss over a number of days can result in a 'sleep debt' with much reduced levels of productivity and attention. Such sleep loss results not only from working night shifts but also on morning shifts with very early start times and from 'on call' situations where it may be difficult to plan when to sleep.

Social and family life

Shift work, especially working rotating shifts, may have an impact on the social life of shift workers. However, this depends on the shift schedule as well as the age, sex, number of children and perhaps the personality of the shift worker. The quality of family life for the worker and the ability to take part in leisure activities may be affected by shift work.

What causes these negative effects?

There are a number of important influences including:

Biological rhythms. We have built-in body clocks to regulate all important body functions. These clocks tell us when to be active and when to rest. They also govern other physiological functions such as body temperature, hormones, digestion and blood pressure. The 24-hour biological rhythms from these clocks do not disappear even if there are changes to the environment (lighting, noise, temperature) and your routine (no sleep, changes of meal routine). Even if you are working nights your body clock will still reduce your body temperature in the early hours of the morning, reduce your blood pressure and stop digestion. This will make you more sleepy and less alert. A night worker trying to sleep during the daytime will find it harder to get to sleep because their body clock is telling them they should be awake. The reduced quality and quantity of sleep will lead to more fatigue as a 'sleep debt' builds up.

Time at work. Human performance tends to deteriorate significantly when people have been at work for more than 12 hours. Below 12 hours the evidence is less clear, and the extent to which fatigue occurs may depend on aspects such as the adequacy of rest breaks, the nature of the work, and the working environment. The effects of fatigue tend to be more marked if the task is monotonous or very repetitive.

Amount of sleep. The daily rest between shifts needs to be adequate to enable shift workers to return to work fully rested. An adult typically needs about seven to eight hours of sleep each night. Rest days are valuable in allowing people to 'recharge their batteries' and to maintain their work performance. The planning of rest days needs to take account of their frequency and the length of 'recovery' time available after blocks of shifts. Shift workers, especially night workers, benefit from regular recovery periods of at least 48 hours. This is because shortened or interrupted sleep over a period of time can result in their spending part of their rest day sleeping.

Shift rotation. A shift pattern which changes about once a week is likely to be more difficult to adjust to than either a more rapidly or a more slowly changing pattern. Current thinking suggests that starting a shift later than the previous one (forward rotation) may create less of a problem than starting a shift earlier than the last one (backward rotation). A typical forward rotation roster would be mornings, afternoons then night shifts. Some shift patterns can result in a short daily rest interval of perhaps only eight hours. This is particularly likely to lead to fatigue through reduced sleep.

Managing the impact of shift work

There is no one solution to the potential health and safety impact of fatigue and shift work. The 'best practice' management approach, which will go beyond what is required by health and safety legislation, is through a multi-component approach which includes:

- careful planning of shift rostering taking into account knowledge of the effects of biological rhythms;
- reviewing maximum hours of duty and time for recovery;
- education of shift workers on sleep routines, nutrition, effects on family and social life, exercise;
- environmental design changes, especially those aspects which can improve alertness such as temperature, lighting, and comfort levels;
- reducing the number of safety-critical tasks planned for the night shift;
- rotating jobs to reduce levels of boredom; and
- providing medical advice for shift workers, especially for those with existing medical conditions.

RELATED CASE STUDIES.

Case study R *Alertness assurance in drivers* gives details of one company which adopted a multi-component approach to shift work and fatigue. Case studies I and J may also give useful tips.

Effective shift communication

In your organisation are the procedures for communicating between departments (eg operations and maintenance) and within departments well-defined and monitored? What arrangements are there for conveying information between shifts on matters such as maintenance in progress, plant out of service, process abnormalities, permits-to-work, etc? How effective are they? Problems with communication have contributed to accidents and near misses in many workplaces.

Effective communication is important in all organisations when a task and its associated responsibilities are handed over to another person or work team. This can occur at shift changeover, between shift and day workers or between different functions of an organisation within a shift (eg operations and maintenance). Although the importance of reliable communication may be recognised, guidance to personnel on how to communicate effectively may be lacking.

What can go wrong?
Unreliable communications can result from a variety of problems including:

- missing information;
- unnecessary information;
- inaccurate information;
- poor or variable quality of information;
- misunderstandings; and
- failing to carry forward information over successive shifts.

High-risk communication situations
Some communication situations are known to be especially liable to problems including:

- during maintenance if the work continues over a shift change;
- during deviations from normal working;
- following an individual's lengthy absence from work; and
- between experienced and inexperienced staff.

Miscommunications and misunderstandings are most likely to occur when the parties communicating have a different understanding of the current state of the process. More time will be needed to communicate when such differing 'mental pictures' exist.

Improving communications
A number of simple steps can improve communications in the workplace:

- carefully specify what key information needs to be communicated;
- aim to cut out the transmission of unnecessary information;
- use aids (such as logs, computer displays) based on the key information needs to help accurate communication;

■   aim to repeat the key information using different mediums, eg use both written and verbal communication;

■   allow sufficient time for communication particularly at shift handover;

■   encourage two-way communication with both the giver and recipient of the information taking responsibility for accurate communication;

■   encourage the asking of confirmation, clarification and repetition;

■   encourage face-to-face communication wherever feasible;

■   try to develop the communication skills of all employees; and

■   aim to set standards for effective and safe communication.

RELATED CASE STUDY

Case study H *Enhancing safe communications at shift handover* gives an example of how shift communication was improved using some of the points listed here.

Focusing on behaviour

While most safety professionals now accept that the majority of workplace accidents are caused by a combination of employee, employer, job and workplace factors, the outdated view was that on-the-job accidents and injuries were the direct result of carelessness and unsafe behaviours. This led to a focus on discipline and training and to the promotion of health and safety incentive programmes which have had little proven success in the long term.

Typical questions asked about people at work are:

■   How can we motivate our workforce to take more care?

■   Why won't people use their personal protective equipment (PPE)?

■   Why did they take that risk?

The traditional reaction to these types of questions is to try to change an individual's attitudes, motivation, risk perception or behaviour through the use of safety posters, safety campaigns or health and safety training. The overriding tendency is to focus on the individual and to exclude other factors relating to the job, the workplace organisation and environment, and the safety climate. However, as illustrated in this guidance, all of these aspects play a role in determining motivation, attitudes, and health and safety-related behaviour at work.

Sometimes arrangements for controlling particular risks make it necessary for people to behave in a certain way, eg to follow a specific procedure or to wear PPE. In high risk situations such reliance on individual behaviour is recommended as a 'last resort' control measure. It is better to eliminate or control the hazard in ways which are not reliant on human behaviour. However, there are ways of promoting higher levels of safe behaviour.

When do we act in a safe way?

If an occupational hazard exists there are three aspects relevant to our decision about behaving safely:

- being aware of the hazard and feeling personally at risk;
- believing that you can control the risks by your actions and the available equipment; and
- behaving safely.

For each aspect there are individual, job and organisational influences to consider. Some key influences on whether a person will behave safely are:

- you perceive the threat as severe;
- you feel personally vulnerable;
- you believe that the available action will be effective;
- you are confidant that you can carry out the protective behaviour;
- the costs of responding are low; and
- your co-workers are carrying out the action.

Being aware of a hazard

People are normally concerned with doing a good job rather than being consciously aware or concerned about the occupational health and safety hazards in their workplace. At appropriate danger signals or for certain critical tasks we need to be able to switch over to a more conscious and focused way of thinking about the risks and controls.

There are a number of influences on whether a person feels at risk from a hazard. A risk is seen as being greater if we perceive it as having severe consequences or if we feel personally vulnerable. For example, a health worker's beliefs about the likelihood of contracting the HIV virus will impact on their perception of the hazard as significant or not. If we feel that the available controls are of limited effectiveness then, in extreme cases, this can lead to us dismissing the threat. Overconfidence, over-optimism or over-familiarity may act to reduce our appraisal of a hazard as significant. There are also well-known biases in individual risk perception which will influence our appraisal of a hazard.

People are bad at judging probability and especially bad at judging risk. This is important because accident rates tend to be higher in groups of people who estimate risks as low. Typically we underestimate the risks attached to our own work. This tendency is greater in familiar situations or where we choose ourselves to take a risk.

People with different roles in the same workplace may judge risks differently. In general we make a lower risk estimation of our own job than of other jobs. For example, workers in the construction industry were asked to estimate the risk of falls by different tradesmen. These included carpenters, tile layers, scaffolders, painters and steel erectors. Each of these groups made consistent judgements but overestimated the risks of trades other than their own by about 10%. They all underestimated their own risks.

To improve our appreciation of risks we need information about the hazard, risk estimates, exposure modes, and available control measures. If individual workers can be made to feel personally vulnerable then this is also helpful. Fear-inducing messages are not usually advisable since people are more likely to reject a threatening fear-inducing message and to assume that the message is for someone else. Constant pressure is needed to make sure that judgements of risk are realistic.

Believing you can control the risks

We ask ourselves how effective our actions might be in controlling the risks. We weigh up the benefits of carrying out safe behaviours against the costs we will incur. For example, a construction worker may weigh up the costs such as physical discomfort of wearing a hard hat in hot weather against the benefits. The 'costs' are typically time, reduced productivity and physical discomfort.

We also consider how effective the available actions or procedures may be and whether we can carry them out. For example if a health worker believes that they will be able to dispose of used needles safely this will influence their safe behaviour.

Behaving safely

The work environment and the health and safety climate influence our safe behaviour. If supervisors and managers appear to condone unsafe behaviour in order to achieve productivity goals then safe behaviour will be less likely. Other barriers to safe behaviour include:

- equipment which is not readily available or in good order;
- not being trained to use the equipment provided;
- a job which is designed in a way which makes it hard to behave safely; and
- other peoples' risk-taking behaviours.

A major influence will be what we see our co-workers doing. So if very few other workers wear hearing protection in a noisy environment then this will not encourage us to comply with the safe behaviour. Managers and supervisors need to be aware that group social norms for safe behaviour exist. They need to set a good example and positively influence such standards of behaviour.

Maintaining safe behaviour is highly dependent on safety culture including group norms and workplace influences. The topic of safety culture is introduced on page 44 of this guidance.

Influencing safe behaviour

There are a number of ways in which you can successfully influence safe behaviour at work, eg:

- by education and training;
- through improved ergonomic design; and
- by introducing a goal-setting and feedback programme.

The approaches complement each other and you may chose to consider more than one.

Beliefs and knowledge are important determinants of safe behaviour. People need to know what the safe behaviour is. **Education** and **training** are therefore vital. Training should cover such key aspects as:

■   knowledge of the work-related health and safety risks;

■   training and feedback in the proper use of safety-related equipment and procedures;

■   awareness of the benefits of carrying out safe behaviour; and

■   the views of managers and co-workers on risk-taking.

Box N shows details from a study by Engels, van der Gulden and Senden (1997)[7] to change the safe lifting practices of nurses to reduce the incidence of back injuries. The study had educational, ergonomic and programme management aspects.

Key aspect	Why important	How achieved
Knowledge and understanding	knowing more about the origin and prevention of musculoskeletal complaints	training of special nurses who then trained others
	understanding the risk factors at work	
Comparison of pros and cons of desired safe behaviour	change of attitude and intention	naming short- and long-term advantages of safe behaviour
Training in proper use of lifting devices	increase in perceived and actual competence in safe working	training of special nurses who then trained others
Opinions of important others (ward sister and work colleagues)	intention to behave safely	participation of colleagues
	confirmation of positive social norms	participation of ward sister
Feedback	maintenance of safe behaviour	refresher course
		feedback to individuals by special nurses

Box N *Education and training of nurses to reduce back pain*

Improving ergonomic design

Changing the method of working to make it easier to work safely or reducing any 'barriers' to safe behaviour are important. This topic is covered in Chapter 3 of this guidance. In the study of safe lifting practices in nurses the ergonomic aspects included introducing new safer working methods through new procedures and reducing barriers through the purchase of lifting devices. Eliminating barriers may be more difficult because obtaining new equipment will cost money and will therefore need to be judged as being a reasonably practicable control measure. It is helpful to set aside resources for such improvements and to ensure that staff are fully trained in the use of new equipment.

Goal-setting and feedback programmes

These programmes are often referred to as behavioural safety management systems. They aim to reduce accidents and ill health by reducing unsafe behaviours and promoting safe behaviours by the workforce. Typically they identify unsafe behaviours associated with previous accidents. A checklist of specific behaviours is developed which is used for observing people's behaviour while they work to provide performance data. Feedback on performance is given individually and on a group basis. Performance goals may be set for the safe behaviours and these can act as motivators. Typical targets for such programmes include the use of personal protective equipment, general housekeeping, access to heights, lifting and bending, and contact with chemicals.

These programmes potentially provide a good opportunity to actively involve the workforce in health and safety since they can be involved in all aspects of the programme. Over-reliance on past accidents as the sole source of the behaviours to be observed could possibly lead to a situation where some behaviours critical to safe operation are overlooked. Risk assessments can be an important means of identifying such behaviours.

The results from such programmes are generally positive with feedback, goal setting, social recognition and praise all being used to reinforce safe behaviour. Such methods have been used successfully to improve the use of protective eye wear and hearing protection. They have also been used with varying degrees of success for other safety-related behaviour and on overall safety performance. Some organisations have fed insights from the behavioural data collected through such programmes into general safety improvements such as the need for improved workplace lighting, or the identification of specific training needs. However, these programmes should not be seen as quick fixes. They demand considerable effort if they are to be implemented effectively. Bear in mind also that the success of such a programme can be highly dependent on the commitment of managers to its implementation and continuation. Worker behaviour is only one factor affecting safety and should not be dealt with in isolation but rather within an effective health and safety management system.

Where such programmes are not successful it can be because the goals which were set were unrealistic or commitment to the process is lacking. Goals need to be agreed in consultation with the workforce and should be:

- visible aspects of health and safety to which most staff can contribute;
- capable of being met without the use of additional equipment, materials or time or serious disruption to work schedules; and
- set within a working environment which is supportive of safe performance.

A number of organisational factors have been found to be associated with good safety performance. The key ones are:

- **Effective communication** - a high level of communication between and within levels of the organisation and comprehensive formal and informal communications.

- **Learning organisation** - the organisation continually improves its own methods and learns from mistakes.

- **Health and safety focus** - a strong focus by everyone in the organisation on health and safety.

- **External pressures** - pressures from outside the organisation including a buoyant financial state of the organisation, and the impact of regulatory bodies.

- **Committed resources** - time, money and staff devoted to health and safety showing strong evidence of commitment.

- **Participation** - staff at different levels in the organisation identify hazards, suggest control measures, provide feedback, and feel they 'own' safety procedures.

- **Management visibility** - senior managers show commitment and are visible 'on the shop floor'.

- **Balance of productivity and safety** - the need for production is properly balanced against health and safety so that the latter are not ignored.

- **High quality training** - training is properly managed, the content is well-chosen and the quality is high. Counting the hours spent on training is not enough.

- **A clean and comfortable working environment** - including general housekeeping, the design and layout of the plant.

- **Job satisfaction** - confidence, trust and recognition of good safety performance impact.

- **Workforce composition** - a significant proportion of older, more experienced and socially stable workers. This group tend to have fewer accidents, lower absenteeism and less turnover.

Box O *Safety performance and related organisational factors*

> **RELATED CASE STUDIES**.
>
> Case studies A and J relate to influencing safe behaviour at work. Many of the cases relate to the provision of training (eg A, B, D, H and R) while others consider the ergonomic design of tools, or the working environment.

Health and safety culture

Every group of people develops a 'culture' - shared attitudes, beliefs and ways of behaving. In an organisation with a good culture everyone puts health and safety high on the list. Everyone shares accurate perceptions of the risks and adopts the same positive attitudes to health and safety. This influences the ways in which individuals in the group handle new events and decisions. They know, for example that they are not expected to react to a problem by cutting corners on health and safety for operational needs.

Some key aspects of an effective culture include.

- good ways of informing and consulting the workforce;
- recognition of the fact that everyone has a role to play;
- commitment by top management to involving the workforce;
- co-operation between employees;
- open two-way communications; and
- high quality of training.

Box O lists many of the factors which influence an organisation's health and safety culture and which are also linked with better safety performance.

The inquiries into major accidents such as the King's Cross Fire, the Clapham Junction Accident, Piper Alpha and the *Herald of Free Enterprise* found faults in the organisational structures and procedures. These were judged to be as important as the technical and individual human failures. After these accidents there is now an emphasis on the need for organisations to improve their safety culture.

Occupational health can also be improved by a climate which considers health issues. For example, a positive health culture may encourage self-protective behaviour such as taking suitable precautions in the face of known health hazards. It can also encourage positive organisational responses to reports of work stress and other psychosocial risks.

Defining safety culture
There are a number of definitions of safety culture but one which covers the key elements is given by HSC's Advisory Committee on the Safety of Nuclear Installations.[8]

> 'The safety culture of an organisation is the product of individual and group values, attitudes, perceptions, competencies, and patterns of behaviour that determine the commitment to, and the style

and proficiency of, an organisation's health and safety management. Organisations with a positive safety culture are characterised by communications founded on mutual trust, by shared perceptions of the importance of safety and by confidence in the efficacy of preventive measures.'

'Health and safety climate' is the term often used to describe the tangible outputs or indicators of an organisation's health and safety culture as perceived by individuals or work groups at a point in time.

Organisational factors associated with a health and safety culture

An effective health and safety management system is the basis for a good health and safety culture. There are certain key aspects of an organisation which will influence its culture. These factors tend to be intangible and often difficult to change and include:

- **Senior management commitment** - crucial to a positive health and safety culture. This commitment produces higher levels of motivation and concern for health and safety throughout the organisation. It is best indicated by the proportion of resources (time, money, people) and support allocated to health and safety management and by the status given to health and safety. The active involvement of senior management in the health and safety system is very important. Managers need to be seen to lead by example when it comes to health and safety.

- **Management style** - influential. A 'humanistic' approach to management involving more regard by managers for individuals' personal and work problems is likely to be effective. This assumes direct and rapid action to identify and resolve individual problems in an appropriately caring and concerned manner.

- **Visible management** - very important for a health and safety culture. Good managers appear regularly on the 'shop floor' and talk about health and safety. Staff need to believe that all their managers are committed to health and safety.

- **Good communications between all levels of employee.** An 'open door' policy may be helpful with direct access to the management hierarchy where appropriate. In a positive culture questions about health and safety should be part of everyday work conversations. This flows from **ownership** - the encouragement of personal responsibility and participation by everyone in health and safety measures.

- **A balance of health and safety and production goals.** People may believe that high standards of health and safety inevitably mean slower work rates. In contrast, production may be seen to be increased through 'cutting corners'. Excessive production pressure creates an atmosphere of distraction and a shortage of time which makes human errors more likely. Excessive pressure may give rise to physical or mental health effects in some employees, and to a higher rate of 'violations' of health and safety rules. In a positive culture health and safety is regarded as important, is promoted, and is not compromised.

Taking steps to influence culture

A step-by-step approach to improving the health and safety culture of an organisation is recommended. The steps of the plan could be as follows:

- review the existing health and safety climate;
- decide on the aspects that have the highest priority for change;
- decide on actions that may change these aspects and take these actions; and
- check and review the actions and then repeat the steps again.

Begin by assessing where you are now and be aware that it takes time to change the culture of an organisation. The ACSNI report[8] provides a comprehensive set of audit questions that you may find particularly helpful. HSE guidance[9] on measuring safety climate contains detailed information on the use of a survey tool. The tool has been developed for organisations to use to assess aspects of their health and safety climate. It consists of a 71-statement employee questionnaire, a guidance booklet and computer software which enables easy analysis of the data generated by the questionnaire. The statements cover aspects such as: organisational commitment and communication, workmates' influence, competence, obstacles to safe behaviour, and risk-taking behaviour. The primary aim of the tool is to promote employee involvement in health and safety and to provide information which can be used as part of a continuous improvement process.

Changes made by managers to improve health and safety will be seen as clear indicators of their commitment. Some suggestions are:

- Review the status within the organisation of the health and safety committees and the health and safety practitioners and increase it if necessary. Give them high visibility.
- Make sure senior management are seen to receive regular reports of health and safety performance and act on them.
- Give publicity to the work of all health and safety committees. Make sure their recommendations are implemented.
- Ensure appropriate health and safety actions are taken quickly and are seen to have been taken.

Action plans to improve health and safety culture should establish that the health and safety procedures:

- are based on a shared perception of hazards and risks;
- are necessary and workable;
- have been developed through employee participation and consultation; and
- are continuously reviewed.

KEY MESSAGES

Find out if there is a problem with shift work and fatigue in your organisation. Pay particular attention to night workers and safety-critical staff. Talk to people doing shift work about how they are coping. Look at the timing of accidents and near misses. Consider the shift schedules of people who make critical mistakes at work. Tackle the problem with a variety of approaches such as shift rostering, improved work environment, better job design and shift work education.

For safer communication pay attention to high-risk situations such as during maintenance, if the work continues over a shift change, or communications between experienced and novice staff. A number of simple steps can improve shift communications.

Accidents and injuries are the result of a combination of employee, employer and job factors. The view that accidents are caused by 'carelessness' is outdated. Nevertheless health and safety behaviour at work is an important topic. Safe behaviour can be influenced by various things including: education and training, improved ergonomic design, and by careful introduction of behavioural management programmes.

The health and safety culture of an organisation is an important factor in achieving and maintaining good health and safety performance. Key factors for a positive culture include: open communications, management commitment and leadership, availability of resources, and the balancing of production and health and safety goals.

CHAPTER FIVE

Getting started

Where do I start?

Having read this far in the guidance you should now have an appreciation of what is meant by 'human factors' and their significance for occupational health and safety. You should also have identified some key issues which may be a problem in your own workplace. There are four key areas where you need to focus your efforts when starting to think about human factors in the workplace. These are:

- human factors in risk assessments;
- human factors when analysing incidents, accidents and near misses;
- human factors in design and procurement; and
- human factors in certain other aspects of health and safety management.

This chapter provides you with some initial starting points for each of these four areas. You will also find it useful to look at the case studies in Chapter 6.

Human factors in risk assessments

Thinking about potential human factors problems and planning ahead is more effective than waiting for problems to occur and then trying to fix them after the event. People issues should be covered in risk assessments such as those required under the Management of Health and Safety at Work Regulations 1992. The Manual Handling Operations Regulations 1992 and the Health and Safety (Display Screen Equipment) Regulations 1992 also need special consideration of human factors issues. These are covered in detail in the specific guidance issued.

A risk assessment is an organised look at your work activities, using the following five steps.

Step 1:   *Look for the hazards*
For human risks you need to consider the range of physical, chemical, biological and psychological hazards. Think also about both the immediate effects of such hazards and any longer-term effects. For example, there may be an immediate physical injury from a violent attack in the workplace with longer-term mental health problems. Remember also that people not only suffer as a result of

hazards at work but they also contribute to the hazards themselves. For example, a human failure by a nurse in not disposing of a needle correctly can lead to a needle-stick injury with a risk of infection by a biological hazard such as the HIV virus. As this guidance has indicated issues such as attitudes to risk, safety culture, ergonomic design and human error are all relevant to this step.

Step 2:   *Decide who may be harmed and how*
Consider which people are most at risk and how the harm may arise. In risk assessments you need to think particularly about certain groups of workers and their needs, eg young, disabled or pregnant workers. Think also about visitors, contractors, and other groups who may not be on the work premises permanently. In deciding how harm may arise you should not assume that people will always follow set procedures and you should allow for the occurrence of human errors and violations.

Since people are involved at all stages in the life cycle of a plant or process, from design to decommissioning, this should be reflected in risk assessments. People do a host of different tasks at work, including: assembly, design, maintenance, operation, cleaning, management, and so on. These need consideration during risk assessments. You should also think about people's behaviour during abnormal and emergency situations, not only during normal work.

When conducting a risk assessment you may find it helpful to consider the task, the individual and the organisational factors. Specialised methods are available to help you to identify specific errors which may occur during a task, but you will also find the results of an activity analysis (see Box P) very informative.

It is often helpful to look at a particular job, task or activity in a given work setting. One approach is to understand what the job actually consists of and what risks are involved. This is known as task or activity analysis. To try it, select a particular activity or task and find the answers to the questions below:

1   Who does this activity?
2   Exactly what tasks/action do they do?
3   What tools or equipment are needed?
4   What decisions are made?
5   What information is needed to do the task?
6   Where does this information come from (people/paper/computers/displays)?
7   How is the task learned and competence assessed?
8   How often is the activity carried out?
9   Where is the task carried out?
10   What is the working environment like (temperature/noise/lighting/etc)?
11   Are there time constraints on the task?
12   What can go wrong? Where is there potential to make errors?
13   How can failures be detected and corrected?
14   What health and safety consequences can result (think about both immediate and longer-term effects)?

You will find it easier if you ask someone who does the activity to walkthrough or talkthrough it with you. The aim is to find out what *really* happens, not just what *should* happen. Working through the questions you will identify problems which need attention and you will be able to feed the results of your analysis into a risk assessment.

BOX P *Analysing an activity*

Step 3:   Evaluate the risks from the hazards and decide whether existing precautions are adequate or if more should be done

You should not rely on the actions of individuals to control a hazard. For example, do not put a warning notice on a dangerous machine and expect everyone to notice, read and comply with the warning. As with all controls, start by trying to eliminate the hazard at source and only rely on individual actions as a final resort. If possible, consider ways of making the situation more 'error tolerant' by improving ways in which people can detect and correct errors and mistakes before they lead to adverse consequences.

In some situations it may be desirable to quantify the risks arising from human failures. There are specific methods available for quantifying the probability of human errors which are used particularly in the nuclear and offshore industries. These techniques were introduced in Chapter 3 of this guidance. If you use these methods, do not fall into the trap of assuming that they are a substitute for upgrading control measures against human failure.

It is important to decide if the risks vary due to human influences. For example, there is a higher likelihood of human error between 2.00 and 5.00 am when physiology dictates that the human body should be asleep. The risks will also be influenced by how well-trained people are, whether they have had sufficient rest before starting a shift, and whether they have taken alcohol or used drugs. You may find useful information in your company's own accident reports and analyses.

Once you know how human factors affect your risks, make sure you incorporate your findings in the design of risk control precautions.

Step 4:   Record your significant findings

If you have fewer than five employees you don't have to record anything but you will probably find it easier if you do.

Step 5:   Review your assessment from time to time and revise it if necessary

You will need to revise your assessment if you make specific changes to work or its organisation, eg changing the number or level of employees, altering the task, equipment or workload, changing the working time pattern.

Human factors when analysing incidents, accidents and near misses

In order to find out where your organisation is vulnerable to human failure and where improvements can be introduced you need to find out more about the human causes of accidents. Chapter 2 introduced you to the ways in which human failures can occur and gave some advice about how to start putting in place prevention strategies. Further advice on finding out causes of accidents is given in another HSE publication (HSG65).[1]

When you are looking at the causes of an accident involving human failures, bear in mind that there will often be more than one cause and that you will need to consider causes and contributing factors that are remote in time and space from the accident (often these will be decisions made by managers) as well as immediate causes (often these will be failures by 'front line' staff). Stopping a re-occurrence of an accident can involve changes to one or more relevant aspects including:

- training and supervision;
- work design;
- procedures and equipment design;
- staff resources;
- work planning and organisation.

Some organisations have found that explaining to accident investigators how human failures arise and what makes them more likely to occur has helped to improve the quality of the accident report and the number of causes and preventive strategies developed as a result.

You can find out more about human factors and potential problems in the workplace by setting up a confidential incident reporting system designed to capture such information. Reports of near misses and other incidents or issues which could have led to an accident are made by staff. It is best if feedback is given to people who report incidents to let them know what actions have been taken and to encourage further reporting. This is a low-cost way of collecting useful information but it does need a supportive health and safety culture to work well.

Human factors in design and procurement

You need to think about human factors when you are designing or redesigning tasks, activities and workplaces. You should also consider such issues when you are designing equipment or systems. Even if you buy in equipment manufactured by others you can try to select items that meet good ergonomic design criteria. Chapter 3 looked at the area of designing for people. You will also find a wealth of useful details of how other companies have tackled this area in the case studies in Chapter 6.

Human factors in other aspects of health and safety management

There are some other issues you need to think about when managing human factors. Chapter 4 looked at some of these including:

- shiftwork and fatigue;
- shift communications;
- influencing safe behaviour; and
- health and safety culture.

These aspects are likely to apply to most workplaces and you may already be looking at some of these in your day-to-day health and safety management. Other areas where you may wish to think about human factors aspects include team working, selection of staff, multiskilling, and setting staffing levels.

How can I do all of this?

There is a lot to do and obviously you will not be able to tackle all of these areas at once. However, you should aim to manage the improvement in human factors in your workplace as you would manage other health and safety aspects. Identify and prioritise the areas where you need to improve and then embark on a continuous cycle of improvement while committing resources to this initiative. Do remember to involve your staff and their representatives in this and try to evaluate the effectiveness of improvements you introduce. You may need to develop some in-company expertise in this area through appropriate training and coaching.

Many managers are familiar with the Plan-Do-Check-Act management cycle. This is just as applicable to human factors issues as to other areas. Table 4 identifies some key areas to consider.

Table 4 *Managing human factors improvements*

Plan
- identify key problem areas or issues for human factors in your workplace (talk to staff and their representatives, look at accident and near miss reports, look at risk assessments);
- prioritise these issues;
- allocate resources;
- identify expertise;
- develop possible solutions or action plans (consider people, their tasks, the work environment and organisational attributes); and
- encourage staff and other people with a stake in the changes to participate in planning and solution development.

Do
- raise awareness of the issues and gain acceptance for the changes;
- implement solutions;
- involve staff and their representatives; and
- communicate about the actions and successes.

Check
- evaluate the effectiveness of actions by asking for the opinions of staff and their representatives;
- check relevant data sources; and
- observe relevant activities.

Act
- if the situation is not satisfactory then identify possible reasons;
- identify alternative steps; and
- encourage participation to solve the situation.

Checklist for human factors in the workplace

You may find it helpful to get started by looking at this checklist which covers many of the points introduced in this guidance.

The job

Tasks should be designed in accordance with ergonomic principles to take into account limitations in human performance. Matching the job to the person will ensure that they are not overloaded and that the most effective contribution to the business results. Physical match includes the design of the whole workplace and working environment. Mental match involves the individual's information and decision-making requirements, as well as their perception of the tasks. Mismatches between job requirements and worker's capabilities provide the potential for human error.

Have you:

	yes	no
■ identified and analysed critical tasks?	☐	☐
■ evaluated the employee's decision-making needs?	☐	☐
■ evaluated the optimum balance between human and automatic systems?	☐	☐
■ applied ergonomic principles to the design of equipment displays including displays of plant and process information, control devices and panel layouts?	☐	☐
■ thought about the design and presentation of procedures and instructions?	☐	☐
■ considered available guidance for the design and control of the working environment including the workspace, access for maintenance, lighting, noise and thermal conditions?	☐	☐
■ provided the correct tools and equipment?	☐	☐
■ scheduled work patterns and shift organisation to minimise impact on health and safety?	☐	☐
■ considered how to achieve efficient communications and shift handover?	☐	☐

The individual

People bring to their job personal attitudes, skills, habits and personality which can be strengths or weaknesses depending on the task demands. Individual characteristics influence behaviour in complex and significant ways. Their effects on task performance may be negative and may not always be mitigated by job design. Some characteristics, such as personality, are fixed and cannot be changed. Others, such as skills and attitudes, may be changed or enhanced.

Have you:

	yes	no
■ drawn up job specifications looking at age, physique, skill, qualifications, experience, aptitude, knowledge, intelligence and personality?	☐	☐
■ matched skills and aptitudes to job requirements?	☐	☐
■ set up personnel selection policies and procedures to select appropriate individuals?	☐	☐

	yes	no
implemented an effective training system?	☐	☐
considered the needs of special groups of employees?	☐	☐
set up monitoring of personal performance on safety for safety critical staff?	☐	☐
provided fitness for work and health surveillance where this is needed?	☐	☐
provided counselling and support for ill health or stress?	☐	☐

The organisation

Organisational factors have the major influence on individuals and group behaviour, yet it is not uncommon for this to be overlooked during the design of work and in the investigation of accidents and incidents. Organisations need to establish their own positive health and safety culture. The climate needs to promote employee involvement and commitment at all levels, emphasising that deviation from established safety standards is not acceptable.

Do you have:

	yes	no
an effective health and safety management system?	☐	☐
a positive safety climate and culture?	☐	☐
arrangements for the setting and monitoring of standards?	☐	☐
adequate supervision?	☐	☐
effective incident reporting and analysis?	☐	☐
learning from experience?	☐	☐
clearly visible health and safety leadership?	☐	☐
suitable team structures?	☐	☐
efficient communication systems and practices?	☐	☐
adequate staffing levels?	☐	☐
suitable work patterns?		

CHAPTER SIX

Case studies: Solutions to human factors problems

Eighteen case studies are given in this chapter to illustrate successful human factors interventions. The cases address a range of problems typically experienced in industry from lost-time accidents to upper limb, back and neck discomfort. The examples are drawn from different industrial sectors and are designed to show how each organisation went about solving their particular problems. In some cases the costs of the solution and the savings made as a result are given. The solutions or control measures used vary from changes to the design of the working environment or tools to increases in employee awareness. Some organisations have developed the solutions in-house. Others have found that employing human factors consultants has led to effective, value-for-money controls.

Do not try to read all of the cases. Select those which are of most interest to you. Use the tables below to look for case studies which are of particular relevance to your industry, human factors problem, or planned control measures.

Table 5 *Case studies listed by health and safety problem*

Problem	Case study
Lost time accidents	A, B, D, N
Vehicle accidents	F, G
Sickness absence	C
Upper limb, neck and back discomfort	I, J, K, L, M
Experience of fatigue	I, J, R
Stress and job dissatisfaction	K, O, P
Human error	E, F, G, N, Q, R
Communication failure	H

Table 6 *Case studies listed by human factors solution/control measure*

Solution	Case study
Design of tools/machines/PPE	A, C, E, G, I, J, M, N, Q
Design of working environment	F, G, L, O, R
Change of process	A, K
Increasing awareness or involving employees	A, B, D, N, Q
Influencing behaviour	A, J
Providing training	A, B, D, H, L, R
Improving communication	B, H
Altering resources	L
Management of tasks	A, I, K, L, M, P

Table 7 *Case studies listed by industrial sector*

Sector	Case study
Manufacturing	A, M
Distribution	B
Aerospace	C
Chemical processing	D, E, H, N
Mining	F, G
Food packaging	I, K
Medical	J
Banking	L
Office setting	O, P
Rail	Q, R

Case Study A Systems approach to safety at shoe manufacturer

Task

The company manufactures an extensive range of shoes for the retail fashion market.

Human factors problems

The company was concerned about the high level of reportable lost time injuries, at 75 per 100 operators per year, and resulting compensation claims associated with its shoe manufacturing operations.

Finding solutions

In 1985, the company adopted a total systems approach to safety. This consisted of:

- the initiation of a safety awareness programme which included basic machine set up and operation, safety principles, and monthly safety meetings;
- a stretching, exercise and conditioning programme;
- the hiring of a full-time human factors specialist;
- specialised training on ergonomics for machine maintenance operators and industrial engineers;
- the purchase of adjustable chairs for all seated operators, and 'anti-fatigue' mats (cushioned rubber mats) for all standing tasks;
- institution of continuous-flow manufacturing, which included operators working in groups, cross-training on the different tasks in a group, and job rotation; and
- redesign of selected machines and workstations for greater adjustability, elimination of awkward postures, and greater ease of use.

Results

As a result of these human factors interventions, compensation insurance premiums dropped by 70% from 1989 to 1995, resulting in a saving of approximately £2 million. During the same time period, the number of reportable lost time injury days dropped from 75 per 100 employees per year, to 19.

The success of the programme was attributed to its total systems perspective, and also to senior management support, employee education and training, and making Human Factors and ergonomics part of everyone's job.

Case Study B Comprehensive human factors changes in petroleum distribution company

Task

The company manufactured and distributed petroleum products to retail outlets throughout the country.

Human factors problems

The company wished to improve health and safety in all aspects of its operations. They employed human factors consultants to examine all aspects of their operations in one (geographical) region for potential improvements.

Finding solutions

Over the course of several years the consultants conducted a comprehensive ergonomic analysis and intervention programme. The programme used a participatory ergonomics approach, ie involving all levels of the company's management and supervision, terminal and filling station personnel, and the truck drivers.

The key components of the programme included:

- an organisational assessment that generated a strategic plan for improving safety;
- equipment changes to improve working conditions and enhance safety; and
- three classes of action items, which included
    - improving employee involvement
    - improving communication
    - integrating safety into the broader organisational culture.

Employee-initiated ergonomic modifications were made to certain items of equipment. New employee-designed safety training methods and structures were implemented. Employees were given a greater role in selecting new tools and equipment related to their jobs. Employees were involved in job analysis, interview design, interviewing and recommending new employees. Thus, the company began recruiting people based on safety predictors known to tanker drivers. The safety predictors included the driver's previous safety record; involvement/leadership in safety activities, an awareness of what they did to achieve safe performance, and understanding why the procedures existed.

Results

Two years after initial installation of the programme, industrial injuries had been reduced by 54%, motor vehicle accidents by 51%, off-the-job injuries by 84%, and lost work days by 94%. Four years later, further reductions had occurred for all except off-the-job injuries, which climbed back to 15%. It is estimated that the greatest reason for the sustained improvement has been the successful installation of safety as part of the organisational culture.

As a direct result of the human factors intervention programme, the company's operations manager estimates that the region saved 0.5% of one percent of the annual cost of petroleum delivery every year. Financially, this means cost reductions of approximately £100 000 each year cumulatively over eight years.

Case Study C Gauge inspection task

Task

In the aerospace industry, an operator on an engine turbine assembly line used a gauge to measure the angle and width between airfoils on the turbines. When an adjustment was necessary, he used a tool to adjust the airfoils, and then re-checked the position. The operator carried out this task for most of his working day.

Human factors problems

Because the dial on the gauge faced away from the operator, he had to bend forward at the waist in order to read it (Figure 5). He often held this position for a long period as he made precise adjustments and readings on the airfoils. The individual had reported sickness absence associated with this task.

Finding solutions

The dial on the gauge was repositioned to face upward so that the operator no longer had to bend forward to make the reading (Figure 6). The modification was made in-house and cost nothing to implement.

Figure 5

Results

The benefits were:

- fewer errors in readings of this critical equipment;
- 20% reduction in the amount of time needed to make readings for the airfoils on the turbine;
- the task is subjectively 'easier' and more comfortable; and
- total elimination of the need to bend forward, and subsequently elimination of reported back problems.

Figure 6

The design of a workstation can force its users into awkward postures, which can lead to discomfort or injury, particularly if the posture must be held for prolonged periods. As illustrated in this example, simple and low cost or even cost-free modifications to the workstation or tool design may allow the operator to work in a more comfortable and safe posture.

Case Study D Introducing a safety awareness campaign

Task

The main tasks carried out at the chemical facilities plant involved the manufacture and use of bulk chemicals, such as hydrofluoric acid. There were also heavy and light engineering operations.

Human factors problems

The company was concerned, in the late 1980s, because the frequency of Lost Time Accidents (LTA) at one of its plants was increasing. In 1988, the LTA frequency* was 1.4, compared to a Chemical Industry Association average, for similar sized facilities, of about 0.4.

Assessing the risk and finding solutions

The company decided to mount a site-wide Safety Awareness Campaign. The campaign had the full and active backing of the site director and other senior management, aimed primarily at a reduction in the LTA frequency. A target of a 50% reduction in frequency, in three years, was set at the beginning of 1990. The central theme was a high-profile, topic-related safety presentation, carried out every second month. It started at the site director's briefing, and was cascaded down by team briefing to every member of the workforce. It concentrated initially on the types of accident occurring most frequently, then moved on to a variety of safety-related topics. It was presented in a 'cartoon style' format by use of flipcharts, with copies, explanatory notes, and personal retention files for every employee. Topics included:

- slips, trips and falls;
- personal protective clothing;
- ladder safety;
- COSHH;
- road safety;
- fire hazards; and
- manual handling.

The cost was approximately £15 000 in the first year, and £5000 per year in subsequent years.

Results

Although the programme did receive some criticism for its simplistic approach, the LTA frequency in the early years of its use fell dramatically, to 0.65 in 1991. The three-year target had thus been achieved in two years. Unfortunately, a period of plateauing and slight regression occurred in 1992, despite the fact that even more effort and resources had been devoted to the programme in 1992/3.

Further analysis showed that 90% of accidents and injuries could be attributed to operator activity or behaviour. In late 1993, a decision was taken to carry the campaign forward on an appropriate behavioural skills approach. An integrated safety culture/behavioural approach/safety

---

* A Lost Time Accident (LTA) *is defined as any injury or accident which results in more than three consecutive days' loss of work. The LTA frequency used in this case is defined as the rate of LTAs per 100 000 person-hours worked.*

audit package was identified. This consists of:

■ Safety culture workshops attended by all senior management, and by as many as practicable of the employees. The site or department's accident performance is given in-depth analysis. It is compared with other industries, the meaning of accident statistics in real terms is examined, and what contributes to accidents and how to avoid them is discussed in detail.

■ A positive, interactive type of safety audit, SUSA (the Safe and Unsafe Acts Auditing) is carried out by team leaders, who are selected and trained to carry out the process. It emphasises the positive side (the 'good' and 'safe' parts) of the task being audited, and uses a simple, but effective question/discussion sequence, designed to encourage the operator to identify his or her own worst possible accident, and to gain his or her commitment to prevent its occurrence. The process recognises the importance of building the individual's self esteem as part of the process of improvement. The auditor is trained to draw from the auditee the suggested means of improvement, and the audit is concluded by getting the auditee's commitment to corrective action, with the promise of the auditor's support in achieving it.

Total expenditure to date has amounted to £150 000 (rising to £325 000 if in-house personnel training or instructional time is included). The LTA frequency, for 1995, has dropped to 0.3, compared with 1.3 before the start of the campaign. This represents a 'saving' of about 215 LTAs. At the average UK cost of one LTA (approximately £10 000), this represents a saving of £2.2m, which more than justifies the outlay. The behavioural approach was identified as the most significant factor behind this improvement. The site set itself a target of 0.1 for the LTA frequency for 1998.

Case Study E Avoidance of error by control interface redesign

Task

As part of the output from a chemical process plant, condensate, water or a water/methanol mixture is loaded into trucks from different storage tanks, and then delivered to its destination.

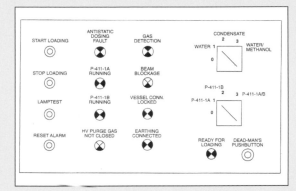

Figure 7

Human factors problems

The existing control interface was not user-friendly (as shown in Figure 7) and truck-drivers occasionally made the wrong selection on the control panel and loaded the wrong liquids into the truck. As a result, drivers were hauling unknown liquids to the wrong destination, a situation which arose on average three times per year. To prevent these errors, the truck-driver was supervised by an operator.

Finding solutions

The solution was to adapt the design of the control panel so that it was compatible with the task in hand, and so that the thought process involved was simplified. The new design consists of a sequential panel which takes the user through the procedure step by step, eliminating the chance of error. The newly designed panel is shown in Figure 8. The new design was piloted in an existing plant. The drivers found the new design much easier to use than the old panel. The company intends to implement it in all future facilities.

Results

The risks of the driver carrying and delivering unknown liquids and the need for operator intervention have both been eliminated, reducing costs and inconvenience to staff.

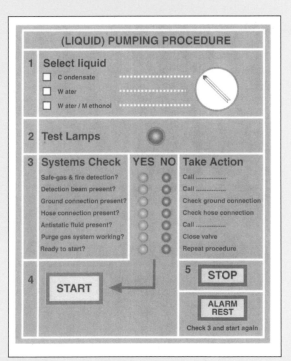

Figure 8

Case Study F Lighting underground locomotive cabs safely

Task

Several types of machine are used underground which need to be driven by a human operator to complete their tasks.

Human factors problems

Safety problems had been identified with the use of a particular type of locomotive. The drivers appeared to be speeding. This was identified through evidence of near misses and damage-only accidents. This overspeeding was of considerable concern as speed limits were designated throughout the mine on reflective boards (to enhance visibility) and were a major topic in driver training.

When the locomotive cab was examined, and the problem was discussed with the drivers, it became clear that the instrument panel, which included the speedometer, was not illuminated. The drivers reported that they could not use their cap lamps to illuminate the panel, because of reflections from the inner surfaces and windscreen of the cab which prevented them seeing where they were going. Thus the drivers did not know the speed at which the locomotive was travelling, and accidents and near misses resulted.

Finding solutions

The solution was simple and involved minimal cost. A fibre optic was routed from the headlamp to the instrument panel, leading to improved illumination while maintaining electrical safety.

Results

The number of near misses and damage-only accidents dropped dramatically once the solution was implemented on all of the particular type of locomotive.

Case Study G Improving human factors in underground vehicle design

Task

Haulage and transport accidents were the major source of accidents in UK mines in the last decade. The 1980s saw an increasing emphasis on the importance of human behaviour as a significant contributory factor in mining accidents.

Human factors problems

In the period 1986 to 1991, nine workmen were killed in accidents, and 96 other workmen received major injuries directly involving or associated with the use of locomotives and free-steered vehicles (FSVs). The main area of concern was poor driver sightlines from the vehicle cabs. As a result, drivers often encountered problems judging the sides and corners of a vehicle when manoeuvring, and seeing people and obstacles close to the vehicle. To overcome these problems, the drivers often had to adopt awkward postures which could ultimately interfere with control operations, or had to place their bodies outside the protective confines of the cab.

Driving errors, influenced by a range of limitations in the design of the vehicles, were influential in determining or contributing to many of the accidents. On locomotives, difficulties in climbing in and out of the cabs caused injuries, and drivers attempted to operate moving vehicles while walking alongside the track and leaning into the cab. Emergency control procedures, such as skid correction, learnt on one vehicle, could not be satisfactorily repeated on other vehicles, which had different control arrangements.

Finding solutions

As much of the machine stock was likely to be used for many years, it became apparent that a systematic study of viable retrofit improvements was necessary to improve safety.

A retrofit index was developed to provide a framework for systematically evaluating vehicle cab designs to identify areas where retrofits would have maximum benefit. The index was based on an extensive series of assessment factors, all of which were likely to influence driver error. The factors included:

- driver sightlines;
- vehicle lighting;
- driver protection;
- access and egress;
- workspace design;
- control and display layouts;
- control and display design;
- labels and instructions;
- seating design;
- communications;
- warning systems; and
- thermal and auditory environment.

Each factor was given a numerical value and weighting which reflected its relative importance to safety. The total scores focused attention on the least safe aspects of cab design for retrofit consideration.

Retrofit ideas for the least safe areas were then generated by teams of ergonomists, colliery staff, manufacturer's staff and representatives from the Mines Inspectorate. For example, on one FSV, 23 retrofit ideas were implemented including:

- The seat was made adjustable: to allow it to be raised to improve sightlines; to allow it to be swivelled to enable the drivers to more easily face the direction of travel; and to allow it to accommodate items on the driver's belt.
- The height canopy could be raised with the seat to improve sightlines, give more headroom, and safer access conditions. The outer support of the canopy was removed to eliminate a potential crushing hazard.
- Increased protection was provided by raising the cab behind the seat, and providing a door across the access aperture.
- Forward sightlines were improved by lowering the front mudguard, locating the headlights on extendible arms, and relocating the hydraulic controls. The arms allowed the headlights to be adjusted so that they shone down the sides of abnormal loads, which reduced the need for the driver to lean out of the cab.
- The handbrake control was modified to provide more working clearance, reduce the risk of accidental operation, and improve access conditions.
- Purpose-designed steps and handholds were provided to reduce the risk of accidents when entering and leaving the cab.
- Important displays were colour coded to minimise the risk of operational errors.
- Pedals were relocated to provide more legroom and improve postures.
- Sharp edges and corners were removed from the access opening.
- The overflow pipe from the radiator was redirected to ground to reduce the risk of injuries through scalding.
- The start interlock control was modified to improve operational reliability and reduce the risk of unauthorised driving practices.

Results

The major improvement was to improve sightlines. For the modified vehicle, there was a 26% reduction in the total area obscured from the driver. This improvement was significant and was achieved from a series of relatively inexpensive, easily implemented changes.

The vehicle was re-assessed after the changes. The total points reduction in the overall score provides a measure of the improvements in safety that can be expected. The percentage improvement for this vehicle was 62%.

The vehicle was also re-examined in risk assessment terms, and the risks were reduced by approximately 50%, by doubling the effectiveness of the hazard control measures.

Perhaps the best indication of the perception of the value of the improvements is a report that the FSV drivers now arrive at work earlier to be the first to get access to the modified vehicle!

Case Study H Enhancing safe communications at shift handover

Task

A large UK oil refinery stabilises in excess of one million barrels per day of crude oil. A five-shift rota system with a 35-day shift cycle was in operation.

Effective shift handover is an important requirement of most shift-working operations. The change-over of tasks and staff can give rise to problems with the transmission or non-communication of critical information. Failures of communication or misunderstanding at shift handover were identified as contributory factors in certain recent industrial accidents, such as the Piper Alpha disaster, and a beach contamination incident at Sellafield.

Human factors problems

A project was initiated to address concern about current shift handover practice. While there had not been any specific incidents where failures of communication at shift handover had been a causal or contributory factor, management had noted potential for improvement in this 'core' site activity.

The project involved collecting information on current shift handover procedures and practice by focusing on one typical area of the refinery. A structured approach with several data collection methods was used, to examine current policies, procedures, documentation and work behaviour, including:

- shift patterns;
- procedures;
- log books;
- training programmes and materials;
- investigation reports into recent incidents;
- observation of 15 shift operator handovers; and
- interviews with personnel at different levels of the organisation.

The review identified the following areas for improvement:

- Most shift log books were unstructured A4 ruled books. There was a lack of guidance on what information should be included, thus style and content varied between individuals. Log book content was mainly historical, with little content indicating what should or might happen in the future. There was no specific reference to safety issues.
- The existing training programme for new recruits included shift handover, but there was no agreed standard against which to assess the adequacy of the trainees' knowledge or behaviour.
- None of the handovers observed had all of the behavioural features present which would define an effective and safe shift handover. For example, in 20% of the handovers observed, there was no evidence of collation of information or making notes in preparation for handover. Many handovers suffered from distractions, in the form of other handovers being conducted simultaneously nearby. Only one of the recipient personnel observed made notes during the handover.

Finding solutions

The main recommendations from the review were:

- implement a pilot scheme of structured logs in one area of the refinery;
- introduce induction and refresher training on safe communication at shift handover; and
- following completion of the pilot project, to introduce structured logs, containing mandatory categories (eg safety, maintenance and technical problems), and discretionary categories (production and quality, personnel matters) site-wide.

Results

Following several weeks in use, a number of improvements resulting from the introduction of structured logs were noted. More information on maintenance and technical problems was being recorded, safety issues were being flagged up, and timings of events were being recorded more consistently. The information in the logs was also easier to access and read, as operators learnt to look for categories in certain positions on the page.

The training programme was well-received by both apprentices and experienced personnel.

During site-wide evaluation of the changes, 70 people were interviewed, representing 22% of those personnel affected by the project: 76% of those people interviewed believed that the introduction of structured logs had led to improvements in how log books were completed; 56% believed that it had led to improvements in how handovers were conducted. Furthermore, 66% of the staff interviewed during the survey felt that there had been a need to improve standards of shift handover, as relevant information had often been lost, missed, or not recorded.

In general, the introduction of structured logs was well received, and helped to facilitate desired changes in behaviour at shift handover. In particular, involving post-holders in the process achieved a degree of commitment which may not have resulted from other methods.

Case Study I Reducing upper limb discomfort in food packing

Task

A food manufacturing company produces and packages many different types of foodstuffs. One of these is custard powder. Two operators at each of the ends of the three production lines pack four 3.5 kg bags of the custard powder from the conveyor into a 14 kg bag, carry the 14 kg bag a short distance to another conveyor and then place the filled bag onto this second conveyor to be palletised in another part of the factory.

Human factors problems

To fill the 14 kg bags with the 3.5 kg bags of custard powder, operators had to work on a metal table 700 mm in height (Figure 9). The depth of the bags meant that many of the (predominantly female) staff were working with their arms and hands raised above shoulder height. Several operators had been off work for periods varying in length from two to seven weeks. Most staff reported that the task was physically very tiring, and a number had reported shoulder and elbow discomfort.

Figure 9

Finding solutions

The solution was to lower the height of the feed conveyor by 500 mm, and to provide a small (400 mm in height) table on which to fill the 14 kg bags rather than the 700 mm table so that the operator was filling the bags at waist height rather than shoulder height (Figure 10). The second conveyor was also lowered and the small table bridged the gap between the two, reducing the necessity for staff to lift and carry the bags. Staff also rotate to another task after 30 minutes. The cost of these changes was less than £1000.

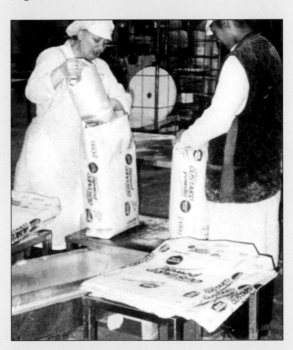

Results

Operators reported a considerable decrease in fatigue when filling the bags at the lower height

Figure 10

table. There has been a marked reduction in time off work in this part of the production line.

Many companies in the food industry use largely automated processes, while the human input is mainly in packing the finished product. The modifications described are a good example of how discomfort can be decreased by observing the task and using principles of human anthropometry (in this case, how tall different sections of the population are) to develop a simple, cheap, effective solution.

Case Study J Employee exercise programme

Tasks

At a large medical supplies manufacturing facility, employees performed various hand and arm intensive tasks. These included attaching needles to suture threads, inspecting suture products, and winding threads for packaging. A few staff also performed manual handling work such as pushing and pulling carts within the sterilisation area.

Human factors problems

Several staff reported symptoms of upper limb discomfort and fatigue. This was proving to be expensive for the company. Indeed, in 1988 the company paid about £200 000 in compensation for human factors-related injuries. Based on medical records, the company estimated that for every 100 employees, 14.3 had reported human factors-related problems.

Finding solutions

In 1990 the company introduced a comprehensive human factors programme featuring:

- an employee exercise programme for all operators;
- engineering changes to the design of individual workstations and jobs; and
- early intervention from the Medical Department to follow up on reported discomfort.

Approximately £60 000 was set aside in the annual budget for this programme.

The company recognised that one factor contributing to work-related discomforts was performing repetitive tasks for long periods without an adequate change in posture or type of activity. The exercise programme was designed to relieve the pressure within the joints and remove some by-products of physical exertion which cause fatigue.

For seven minutes in the morning and again in the afternoon, all personnel stop their production tasks and participate in a series of light exercises accompanied by music. The type of exercise depends on the task they perform and the body area most likely to be stressed. For example, a common exercise for those performing hand intensive work requiring pinching is gently moving each finger up and down.

Results

As expected, employees were initially reluctant to perform stretches and exercises at work. However, after about six months, all employees were actively participating through their work teams. Each team decided when to take their exercise breaks and selected their own exercises. Initially the sessions were led by external exercise physiologists, but now team leaders have received the relevant training and conduct the sessions.

Employee feedback has been very positive, and operators are reporting greater physical comfort following their exercise session. Employee awareness of risk factors has been raised, such that now approximately 70% of the ideas for changes to the workplace come from the production operatives.

The company recognised that the exercise programme alone (without changes to workstation design) would not have produced such a significant increase in employee comfort and health. However, by relieving pressures in joints and muscles, particularly in the upper limbs, the exercises complemented a wide range of changes to the work area which brought about other improvements in terms of the operators' postures, forces applied, and repetitiveness. The latest medical records now show that out of every 100 employees, approximately 2.9 report human factors-related problems annually. Annual payments for related compensation claims have decreased steadily, to the point where no money was spent for such claims in 1994.

Exercises which relieve musculoskeletal stresses can be effective for a wide range of job tasks, from upper limb-intensive industrial tasks, to keyboard tasks such as copy-typing. They can be useful as part of an overall human factors programme which includes relevant engineering changes to the work areas and training of the operators.

Case Study K Easter egg and chocolate box packing

Tasks

Easter eggs are packaging-intensive, and much of the packing process is carried out by hand. Previously, eight separate components were assembled by hand, and most of these components arrived as cardboard flat-packs which then had to be folded and bent into the correct shape. The operators on this task were paid piecework rates dependent on the number of eggs they assembled during a shift.

During the production of boxes of chocolates, two layers of chocolates in a plastic mould tray, a pad of corrugated cardboard, and the 'unit key' (ie to identify the filling in the chocolate) need to be packed into different-size boxes. Previously, the boxes were presented to the operator on a moving conveyor, and as they went past, different operators had to put different components (the chocolates, the mouldings in which they sit, the cardboard pad, and information leaflets) into the boxes in a flow assembly operation.

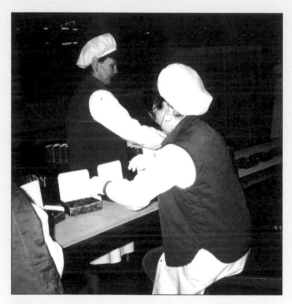

Figure 11

Human factors problems

The original Easter egg packaging task (Figure 11) required many movements of the hand and wrist, eg bending and folding of the cardboard, and snapping a plastic cover over the eggs required force with a pinch grip. The company physiotherapist and other medical department staff were seeing people from the egg packaging department with upper limb discomfort.

In the chocolate box assembly, the operators' work rate was determined by the conveyor. The box design made it difficult to place the components accurately in the boxes when the conveyor was moving.

Finding solutions

The company doctor, the operations manager and the industrial engineer for the site assessed the tasks involved, and determined that certain elements needed to change.

Investment was planned for the Easter egg assembly line, to change it from a piecework operation. The packaging of the Easter eggs was redesigned to remove the cardboard bending and the snapping shut of the plastic mould, and as a consequence, the number of uncomfortable wrist and hand movements was greatly reduced. The pay structure also changed, from piecework to salaried work. The 'after' workstation is shown in Figure 12.

For the chocolate box assembly, the engineers devised a mock-up belt/workstation arrangement to trial with the operators, in which the rate of completion of the task was determined by the operator, not by the conveyor. In addition, the whole assembly task for a box was to be done by a single operator, rather than one operator putting one component into the box. The engineers worked out the best angle for viewing the components, for taking them off the conveyor, and for assembling them without twisting and turning. After testing out this design with the operators, the new line was built and installed. The new workstation is shown in Figure 13.

The costs of the changes were not measured.

Results

Figure 12

For the Easter egg packing:

■ fewer cases of wrist and hand discomfort are now reported to the medical staff;
■ overall efficiency of production has improved;
■ the number of units damaged has decreased, and the visual quality of the finished product has improved;
■ the amount of material (chocolate, plastic and cardboard) wasted has decreased;
■ staff morale has improved;
■ the egg production workflow is easier to manage and regulate; and
■ there is less job rotation, because the nature of the job has improved.

Figure 13

For the chocolate box packing:

■ operator comfort has increased, as the adjustability in each workstation can be used to meet each operator's needs;
■ assembly quality has improved, as the operators are no longer trying to put the components into a moving box; and
■ lighting conditions have improved as large machines which caused shadows have been removed.

Packaging operations are performed manually in a range of different industries. As these case studies illustrate, the operator is required to use positions of the hand and wrist which can lead to upper limb discomfort, especially when combined with high forces or repetition. The company has benefited in both production efficiency and staff well-being and physical comfort by recognising risks within the task, and investing in ergonomics changes to the tasks and the packaging materials.

By designing the workstations well, and giving the operators control over the time taken to do the task, quality, productivity, job satisfaction and operator comfort have improved.

Case Study L 'Clearing' operation

Task

The process known to banks and building societies (and the public) as 'clearing' of cheques is carried out on a nightshift basis. An 'encoding machine' is used to key in data (eg the amount on the cheque, the account number etc) into the financial system. Operators sit at the encoding machines feeding the cheques into one part of the machine with their left hand. The cheques are then conveyed one-by-one through to a display area. The operator views the cheque, keys in the relevant data with their right hand, using a numerical keypad, and the cheque is conveyed to a collecting tray to the right of the machine. The operators perform between 12 000 and 14 000 keystrokes per hour.

Human factors problems

Several of the encoding staff were reporting discomfort and pain in their right hands. Two staff had been diagnosed with upper limb disorders, and five other staff were experiencing discomfort serious enough to cause them to take time off work. Several encoders had also reported back and shoulder discomfort.

Figure 14

Finding solutions

The encoding tasks, equipment and environment were surveyed by ergonomics consultants. The right hand discomfort was likely to be caused by the high keying rates, the lack of breaks from keying, and the effect of resting the wrist on the edge of the encoding machine while keying. The back and shoulder discomfort was likely to be caused by the design of the encoding machine - to operate the keypad, the encoders' hands were used in different locations at different heights, causing twisting of the upper body. Furthermore, the backrests of the encoders' chairs were not adjustable in height and tilt, and no footrests were available (Figure 14).

Unfortunately, there was nothing that could be done to alter the design of the encoding machines themselves. However, the company implemented several measures to improve other aspects of the task (Figures 15 and 16), including:

- purchasing new chairs, which were adjustable in seat height, backrest height and tilt, and armrest height;
- purchasing footrests;

Figure 15

- changing the work patterns by rotating staff to other jobs which did not require the use of the encoding machines;
- encouraging staff to take breaks more frequently;
- training the encoders in ergonomics, to ensure that they understood the importance of breaks, and to enable them to use the adjustability provided in the equipment to match the workstation to their own particular body size and requirements;

- training staff in relaxation exercises to relieve stress;
- employing extra temporary staff to cover busy times; and
- altering the lighting, heating and ventilation in the area.

The cost of the changes was approximately £750 per operator, which the company believed to be a very worthwhile investment to reduce sick leave and the possibility of compensation claims.

Figure 16

Results

Survey data from the same staff collected before and after the changes showed a decrease of approximately 25% in the symptoms of shoulder, arm, wrist, hands, neck and back discomfort. Furthermore, staff reported subjectively that they were more comfortable and less fatigued as a result of the changes to the equipment and to the working practices.

This case study illustrates that even though the main cause of the problems (the encoding machines) could not be altered, it is still possible to make people more comfortable by paying close attention to all parts of their working area, and to the working practices themselves. Ultimately though, purchasers should put pressure on manufacturers to design equipment which meets the needs of the human user as well as of engineering constraints.

Case Study M Assembly and finishing of door locking mechanism

Task

The assembly and finishing of vehicle door locking mechanisms is carried out as part of the operations in the automotive industry. The assembly is carried out by a team of eight to twelve people.

The operators stood while carrying out the assembly tasks and often used one workstation for the whole of the shift. The nature of the work required small upper body movements with the arms raised at some of the workstations. Gross muscle activity was limited to walking to other workstations to assist colleagues or to collect parts from storage bins. This was dependent upon the size of the parts used (many more smaller than larger parts could be stored at the workstation, requiring the operator to collect from storage bins less frequently) and whether operators 'helped' each other by filling parts bins for colleagues. On average, operators moved from their workstation (two steps or more) 12 times per hour.

Human factors problems

Some operators had reported upper limb, neck, and back discomfort. Sitting at the task could not be achieved satisfactorily because the bench design did not allow adequate knee clearance.

Finding solutions

The assembly cells were recently purpose-built at a significant investment to suit the production requirements of the company's clients. Therefore, a large redesign and refit was not financially viable in the short to medium term.

Video recordings were made of the operators at the assembly cell over half a shift. This was analysed to classify type, duration and frequency of movements for the assembly tasks. A checklist was also completed with the operator at each workstation in the cell to clarify the nature of the tasks.

The main recommendations were to:

■ limit the time spent at one workstation to 2 hours and include a formal 10 minute rest break;
■ rotate operators around the tasks over the course of the shift;
■ provide a low footrest to place each foot on alternately while working;
■ make sure operators service their own parts requirements;
■ adjust the workstation height so the top of the work jig is 950 mm above the standing surface (implemented using various spacers and cut away sections);
■ reposition the jigs to the front of the workstation so that the task can be carried out close to the operator's body;
■ position parts bins symmetrically to prevent twisted postures and encourage a more even use of both hands;
■ mock up a series of personal workstands for the operators to try. These would fit onto the top of the workstation and use universal small parts containers;
■ re-assess the requirement for work stools in light of the alterations; and
■ carry out full manual handling assessment of tasks at this cell as some heavy loads were being lifted from floor level.

Most of the physical alterations such as workstation heights, moving jig positions, constructing workstands and footrests have been arranged in-house at low cost using parts and facilities already available.

Results
One of the local factory inspectors had previously suggested that operators be provided with seats. An immediate benefit to the company of the assessment and recommendations was that the inspector reviewed his opinion in favour of trying out and assessing the effect of the new options.

Early results indicate that operators are much more comfortable using the redesigned workstations.

Case Study N Introduction of a mini-crane in a chemical plant

Task

Maintenance, hoisting and transport tasks are regularly carried out as part of ongoing operations in chemical plants.

Human factors problems

The following problems were identified during hoisting and transport activities and the maintenance of pumps and electric motors:

- considerable inefficiency due to inadequate hoisting facilities and tools;
- unsafe actions required of workers, eg climbing onto equipment; and
- tripping accidents and physical injuries.

Finding solutions

An ergonomics study conducted in consultation with operations and maintenance staff resulted in a set of functional specifications for a new crane. A design of mini-crane was found to fit the required specifications.

The mini-crane was used for a trial period of three months at a chemical plant, following which management approved the lease of several mini-cranes and the use of the mini-crane specifications in new building projects.

The ergonomics study cost approximately £7000. Each mini-crane is leased for approximately £6500 per year.

Results

Benefits included:

- reduction in the use of oversized cranes, tackles and beams, scaffolding and inadequate tools;
- reduction of operational work-hours;
- elimination of unsafe actions and physical strain; and
- increased staff motivation.

A cost/benefit analysis was performed on the use of the mini-crane. The reduction in the use of oversized cranes, scaffolding costs, and work-hours resulted in a saving of £28 000 per year. In addition, when mini-cranes were used from the beginning in two new building projects, instead of using permanent facilities, the projects reported savings of £7000 and £45 000.

Case Study O Increasing job satisfaction through simple layout changes

Task

Four staff working in the typing support services department of the organisation used Display Screen Equipment (DSE) for 90% or more of their working day. The main work of the department was copy-typing, with occasional task variety in the form of filing, photocopying, or envelope-filling.

Human factors problems

Staff found the environmental design and workstation layout in this department very restricting (although potentially good facilities and plenty of space were available). Although the total worksurface space provided for each member of staff was generous, each person's workstation consisted of two parts - one single surface desk for paperwork in one part of the room, and a split-level desk for DSE use facing the wall in another part of the room.

In theory, this arrangement was intended to give staff an opportunity to physically and mentally 'get away' from the DSE. In practice, as so much of the job involved DSE use, it meant that they spent 90% of their time working at the (small) split level desks, at which there was not enough space to arrange paperwork etc. Staff working at these desks were seated very close together, adopted poor postures because of the cramped layouts, and sat facing a blank wall.

Finding solutions

In 1992 the organisation asked ergonomists to help them meet the requirements of the incoming Regulations on Display Screen Equipment. These workstations were examined and considered to be unsatisfactory in many ways. Recommendations were made for alternative layouts, and in consultation with the four people in this office, the layout was totally re-planned. The same equipment was used, but in very different layouts in the room. The organisation did not incur any costs in making these changes, apart from the cost of the ergonomist's time, at approximately £750.

Results

Each user now has much more control over their working environment. Each has an L-shaped workstation with all the equipment they need close to hand. Each user has the display screen positioned correctly at right-angles to the windows, and they no longer face a blank wall (Figure 17). The layout was arranged so that each user also has a radiator and a window (with blinds) next to their workstation, so they can adjust the temperature, lighting and air flow to their own needs. Postures at the workstations are now much better, and people have much more personal space, as the area is less cramped.

The users all much prefer the new arrangement, reporting that their satisfaction with many areas of their workplace has increased including:

■ greater comfort;
■ it is subjectively easier to take necessary breaks from keying, as the new layout means it is not so clear that someone is absent from the row of typing stations;

Figure 17

- the lighting conditions are better, with everyone having easy access to a window;
- the office is less draughty;
- it is more sociable, as they no longer face the wall (this increases social interaction, and enhances the feeling of being part of a team); and
- they feel less like 'typing robots'.

Other benefits include tidier cabling, and better communications with each other. Furthermore, as they no longer have their backs to the door, they do not have to twist round to talk to people coming to deliver or collect work.

This case illustrates the importance of a comfortable physical layout of a workstation. It also illustrates that where several people use an environment, they interact with each other, and these interactions can affect performance. In the previous arrangement, people felt socially inhibited (as they would disturb other people if they spoke), and inhibited from taking breaks (as it was very clear when someone was not there) because they were packed so close together in a row.

Case Study P Data processing department planning

Task

In 1982 a parcels delivery company set up a data processing (DP) department to prepare the information relevant to invoicing for the parcels delivery service. This information was manually extracted from the 'consignment note' which accompanied each set of parcels, and typed into the mainframe-based computer system for weekly invoicing of customers. Forty thousand of these consignment notes needed to be processed every day by the DP department.

Human factors problems

When the department was being set up, management were concerned about the job satisfaction, health, and safety of the staff who would be working there. They knew that data processing jobs could be very repetitive and stressful, leading to errors and fatigue. They wished to avoid this.

Finding solutions

The management looked at how data processing operations were carried out in computer bureaux (in other organisations), and this confirmed their view: the data processing was very repetitive, with rates in excess of 15 000 keystrokes per hour expected from operators. Operators were also paid on piecework rates according to the number of keystrokes they performed, which increased the intensity and stress associated with the job.

In consultation with the operators, the parcels delivery management agreed to implement several measures to reduce the problems caused by repetitive data entry. They agreed to:

- limit the number of keystrokes to a departmental average of 13 000 keystrokes per hour;
- rotate operators regularly onto jobs that did not require such intensive keypunching;
- take breaks at set times; and
- pay the operators by salary rather than on piecework rates.

Results

Over the twelve years that the department has been in operation, there have been no claims made against the company for upper limb disorders, despite the intensive nature of the operation.

With the introduction of new technology, this data processing operation will disappear. The company is retraining staff and finding other jobs for them consisting of more varied tasks, within the organisation.

This case study illustrates that paying attention at the start to the ergonomics and organisational aspects of an operation which is intensive in nature (and therefore relatively higher-risk than general office tasks), can help to minimise the types of upper limb discomfort which can be associated with intensive data-entry tasks.

Case Study Q Quality assurance of driver-only operation

Task

The company was moving from running passenger trains with a driver and a guard to driver-only operation. Additional equipment was being installed on each platform to enable the driver to see along the train.

Human factors problems

An earlier driver-only scheme had run into problems because of human factors concerns. The company wanted to ensure successful implementation of a large driver-only scheme involving over 100 stations. It was important that the risks to passengers entering or leaving the train must not be increased as a result of the change in arrangements.

Finding solutions

The company employed a human factors consultant as part of the quality assurance process for implementation. The human factors review consisted of:

- checking that the cab design was suitable for driver-only operation considering issues such as seating position and viewing angles;
- evaluating alternative methods of driver-only operation from an ergonomic perspective; and
- conducting ergonomic audits of the equipment provided at all locations before the scheme was brought into full operation.

The company ensured that drivers' representatives and union officials were fully briefed about the findings of the audits. A system was set up to resolve any minor problems rapidly. A user group was also set up to ensure future problems were identified and resolved and to create a sense of ownership for the scheme.

Results

The extensive driver-only scheme was brought into operation without problems and has proved to be one of the most successful such schemes in the UK to date.

This case study demonstrates the benefits if suitable advice is sought early in the life of a project. Too often human factors issues are addressed too late in a project for cost-effective solutions to be implemented.

Case Study R Alertness assurance in drivers

Task
The company employs a number of drivers of passenger trains. Drivers are classed as safety critical staff.

Human factors problems
Driving involves spending long periods of time in the cab of a train. Drivers can be susceptible to fatigue and loss of alertness which could increase the probability of a human error. Drivers are shift workers and may have disturbed sleep patterns and shortened sleep periods. The company wanted to modify the rosters of drivers without compromising safety levels. They were particularly concerned with maintaining high levels of alertness among drivers.

Finding solutions
The company asked human factors consultants to undertake a survey of drivers to establish if there was a problem with fatigue and levels of alertness. The survey covered both work-related and personal issues. Ninety per cent of drivers completed the survey. Some volunteer drivers were also given a physical activity monitor to record alertness and microsleeps. These drivers also completed a daily activity log.

As a result of the findings shift rosters were redesigned to reduce the disruptions of circadian rhythms (biological body clock governing the 24-hour sleeping/waking cycle). The changes include a clockwise start time shift rotation and a reduction in the number of consecutive days worked.

Changes to the cab environment which were designed to improve alertness were proposed. These included improvements to the seat and armrest adjustment, installation of central window blinds and a cab fan. Drivers would also be provided with facial wipes.

A quiet room with a reclining chair was provided in one of the depots for drivers to take advantage of a short nap or period of relaxation between train turns if they so desired.

Shift work education was provided for drivers and their partners. This lifestyle education covered sleep management, shift work and nutrition, family and social issues, health and safety issues and circadian physiology.

Results
The company has estimated that the changes are likely to reduce safety-related incidents caused by 'driver error'. The annual safety benefit is estimated at £51 000. Additional benefits may result from reduced levels of absenteeism and sickness.

Early signs are that the new rosters are liked by drivers. The study is leading to a culture change in how the organisation views fatigue and alertness. Other train-operating companies are showing interest in the findings.

This study is a good example of the benefits of considering fatigue and alertness from a number of approaches rather than just focusing on duty-time limits.

Acknowledgements

HSE commissioned Matsu and Systems Concepts Limited to gather information for the case study material in this publication. We would like to thank them and to acknowledge the generosity of the following companies who supplied information for case studies to help compile this publication:

Ameritech, USA

BP Oil Ltd, Grangemouth, UK

British Nuclear Fuels plc, Preston, UK

Cadbury Ltd, Birmingham, UK

Cambit, Cambridge, UK

Delta-T Devices Ltd, Cambridge, UK

Department of Design and Environmental Analysis, Cornell University, USA

Department of Human Work Sciences, Lulea Tekniska Universitet, Sweden

Design Triangle, Cambridge, UK

Ergonomics and Safety Department, University of Southern California, USA

Ergonomics Training Centre, London, UK

Ergotech, South Africa

ErgoWeb Inc, USA

European Broadcasting Union, Switzerland

Ferris Associates, Bishops Stortford, UK

Imperial College of Science, Technology and Medicine, London, UK

International Mining Consultants Ltd, Burton-on-Trent, UK

Lehrstuhl für Forstliche Arbeitswissenschaft und Angewandte Informatik, Germany

Open Ergonomics, Loughborough, UK

Rockwell LVS (UK) Ltd, UK

Royal Mail and Royal Mail International, Swindon, UK

Shell International BV, The Netherlands

Thameslink, UK

The Keil Centre, Edinburgh, UK

The Raymond Corporation, USA

TNT United Kingdom, UK

Trades Union Congress, London, UK

Glossary

Active errors An active human error is an intended or unintended action that has an immediate negative consequence for the system.

Human error probability The probability that an error will occur during the performance of a particular job or task within a defined time period.

Human reliability The probability that a task will be successfully completed within a required minimum time.

Human-machine interface The boundary across which information is transmitted between the process and the worker, eg analog displays, VDUs.

Latent errors An erroneous action or decision where the negative consequences are apparent only after a period of time and when combined with other conditions or events.

Mistakes Errors arising from a correct intention that led to incorrect action(s). These errors may arise from lack of knowledge or incorrect diagnosis.

Performance shaping factors (or performance influencing factors) Factors that influence the effectiveness of human performance and the likelihood of errors. Examples include design of displays and controls, training, fatigue, environmental and job design factors.

Root cause The most basic cause of an incident or accident that can reasonably be identified and that managers have the control to fix.

Slips Errors in which the intention is correct but failure occurs when carrying out the action required. Slips occur in routine, highly familiar tasks.

Violation Any deliberate deviation from the rules, procedures or instructions drawn up for health and safety.

Professional societies

Professional societies whose members include experts in human factors, psychology and ergonomics include:

The British Psychological Society, St Andrews House, 48 Princess Road East, Leicester LE1 7DR

The Ergonomics Society, Elms Court, Elms Grove, Loughborough, Leicestershire LE11 1RG

Society of Occupational Medicine, 6 St Andrew's Place, Regents Park, London NW1 4LB

References

1   *Successful health and safety management* HSG65 (Second edition) HSE Books 1997
     ISBN 0 7176 1276 7

2   *Guidelines for preventing human error in process safety* American Institute of Chemical Engineers
     1994 ISBN 0 8169 0461 8

3   *Improving compliance with safety procedures: Reducing industrial violations* Report HSE 1995
     Web only: www.hse.gov.uk/humanfactors/comah/procedures.htm

4   *Real solutions, real people: A managers' guide to tackling work-related stress* HSE Books 2003
     ISBN 0 7176 2767 5

5   *Work stress: Advice on its prevention and management* SHE15 Loss Prevention Council Report 1998
     ISBN 0 9021 6788 X

6   Kirwin B A *A guide to practical human reliability assessment* Taylor and Francis 1994
     ISBN 0 7484 0111 3

7   Engels J A, van der Gulden and Senden T F 'Prevention of musculoskeletal complaints in
     nursing: Aims, approach and content of an ergonomic-educational programme' *Safety Science*
     1997 **27** 141-148

8   ACSNI *Human Factors Study Group: Third report – Organising for safety* Report HSE Books 1993
     ISBN 0 7176 0865 4

9   *Health and safety climate survey tool: A tool to help your organisation improve health and safety performance
     through employee involvement* CD Rom HSE Books 1997 ISBN 0 7176 1462 X

Further reading

Chapter 2

Individual differences in accident liability: A review CRR175 HSE Books 1998 ISBN 0 7176 1575 8

Reason J *Human error* Cambridge University Press 1991 ISBN 0 5213 1419 4

Reason J *Managing the risks of organisational accidents* Ashgate 1997 ISBN 1 84014 105 0

Turner B and Pidgeon N *Man-made disasters* (Second edition) Butterworth Heinemann 1997
ISBN 0 7506 2087 0

Chapter 3

Ergonomic design

A pain in your workplace? *Ergonomic problems and solutions* HSG121 HSE Books 1994 ISBN 0 7176 0668 6

Work with display screen equipment. Health and Safety (Display Screen Equipment) Regulations 1992 as amended by the Health and Safety (Miscellaneous Amendments) Regulations 2002. Guidance on Regulations L26 (Second edition) HSE Books 2003 ISBN 0 7176 2582 6

Kroemer K *Fitting the task to the human: A textbook of occupational ergonomics* (Fifth edition) Taylor and Francis 1997 ISBN 0 74 840665 4

Lighting at work HSG38 (Second edition) HSE Books 1997 ISBN 0 7176 1232 5

Manual handling: Solutions you can handle HSG115 HSE Books 1994 ISBN 0 7176 0693 7

Nicholson A S and Ridd J E (eds) *Health, safety and ergonomics* Butterworths 1988 ISBN 0 40 802386 4

Pheasant S E*rgonomics, work and health* Macmillan 1991 ISBN 0 33 348998 5

The law on VDUs: An easy guide: Making sure your office complies with the Health and Safety (Display Screen Equipment) Regulations 1992 (as amended in 2002) HSG90 (Second edition) HSE Books 2003 ISBN 0 7176 2602 4

Upper limb disorders in the workplace HSG60 (Second edition) HSE Books 2002 ISBN 0 7176 1978 8

Designing jobs for mental well-being

Arnold J, Robertson I T and Cooper C L *Work Psychology: Understanding human behaviour in the workplace* (Second edition) Pitman 1995 ISBN 0 273 60324 8

Stress research and stress management: Putting theory to work CRR61 HSE Books 1993 ISBN 0 7176 0684 8

Mental well-being in the workplace: A resource pack for management training and development Guidance HSE Books 1998 ISBN 0 7176 1524 3

Hackman J R and Oldman G R *Work redesign* Addison-Wesley 1980 ISBN 0 201 02779 8

An assessment of employee assistance and workplace counselling programmes in British organisations CRR167 HSE Books 1998 ISBN 0 7176 1519 7

Organisational interventions to reduce the impact of poor work design CRR196 HSE Books 1998 ISBN 0 7176 1632 0

Writing procedures

Guidelines for writing effective operating and maintenance procedures American Institute of Chemical Engineers 1996 ISBN 0 8169 0658 0

Designing warnings for maximum effect

Edworthy J and Adams A *Warning design: A research perspective* Taylor and Francis 1996 0 74 840467 8

Laughery K R, Wogalter M S and Young S L (eds) *Human factors perspectives on warnings: Selections from Human Factors and Ergonomics Society annual meetings* 1980-1993 Human Factors and Ergonomics Society 1994 ISBN 0 945289 02 2

Safety signs and signals. The Health and Safety (Safety Signs and Signals) Regulations 1996. Guidance on Regulations L64 HSE Books 1996 ISBN 0 7176 0870 0

Human reliability assessment

Study group on human factors: Second report Report HSE Books 1991 ISBN 0 11 885695 2

Chapter 4

Fatigue and shiftwork

Monk T H and Folkard S *Making shiftwork tolerable* Taylor and Francis 1992 ISBN 0 85 066822 0

Moore-Ede M *The 24-hour society: The risks and challenges of a world that never stops* Piatkus 1993 ISBN 0 7499 1255 3

Shiftwork, health and safety: An overview of the scientific literature 1978-1990 CRR31 HSE Books 1992 ISBN 0 7176 1119 1

Effective shift communication

Effective shift handover: A literature review OTO1996/003 HSE 1996
Web only: www.hse.gov.uk/research/otopdf/1996/oto96003.pdf

Focusing on behaviour

Hale A R and Glendon A I *Individual behaviour in the control of danger* Elsevier 1987 ISBN 0 444 42838 0

Sulzer-Azaroff B 'The modification of occupational safety behaviour' *Journal of Occupational Accidents* 1987 **9** (3) 177-197

Health and safety culture

Developing a safety culture Confederation of British Industry 1990 ISBN 0 85201 361 2

Play your part! How offshore workers can help improve health and safety Guidance HSE Books 1994 ISBN 0 7176 0786 0

Printed and published by the Health and Safety Executive   02/07   C30